DATE DUE

Growing Up with SCIENCE®

Third Edition

2

Atmosphere –Cable television

Marshall Cavendish
Reference
New York

Marshall Cavendish
99 White Plains Road
Tarrytown, NY 10591

www.marshallcavendish.us

© 2006 Marshall Cavendish Corporation
© 1987, 1990 Marshall Cavendish Limited

GROWING UP WITH SCIENCE is a registered trademark
of Marshall Cavendish Corporation

Library of Congress Cataloging-in-Publication Data

Growing up with science.— 3rd ed.
    p. cm.
  Includes index.
  Contents: v. 1. Abrasive-Astronomy — v. 2. Atmosphere-Cable television —
v. 3. Cable travel-Cotton — v. 4. Crane-Electricity — v. 5 Electric motor-
Friction — v. 6. Fuel cell-Immune system — v. 7. Induction-Magnetism —
v. 8. Mapmaking-Mining and quarrying — v. 9. Missile and torpedo-Oil
exploration and refining — v. 10. Optics-Plant kingdom — v. 11. Plasma
physics-Radiotherapy — v. 12. Railroad system-Seismology — v. 13.
Semiconductor-Sports — v. 14. Spring-Thermography — v. 15. Thermometer-
Virus, biological — v. 16. Virus, computer-Zoology — v. 17. Index.
  ISBN 0-7614-7505-2 (set)
  ISBN 0-7614-7507-9 (vol. 2)
  1. Science—Encyclopedias.

Q121.G764 2006
503—dc22

                                                    2004049962
                              09 08 07 06 05 6 5 4 3 2 1

Printed in China

CONSULTANT

Donald R. Franceschetti, Ph.D.

Dunavant Professor at the University of Memphis

Donald R. Franceschetti is a member of the American
Chemical Society, the American Physical Society, the
Cognitive Science Society, the History of Science Society,
and the Society for Neuroscience.

CONTRIBUTORS TO VOLUME 2

Martin Clowes   Tom Jackson

Dan Gilpin   Nathan Lepora

Rob Houston   Jim Martin

Marshall Cavendish

Editor: Peter Mavrikis

Editorial Director: Paul Bernabeo

Production Manager: Alan Tsai

The Brown Reference Group

Editors: Leon Gray and Simon Hall

Designer: Sarah Williams

Picture Researchers: Clare Newman and Helen Simm

Indexer: Kay Ollerenshaw

Illustrators: Darren Awuah and Mark Walker

Managing Editor: Bridget Giles

Art Director: Dave Goodman

PICTURE CREDITS

Cover inset: National Aeronautics and Space Administration

7E Communications: 237; **Airbus:** 224; **Art Explosion:** 162; **BMW (GB) Ltd.:** 140 (*center*); **CERN Geneva:** 136, 205; **Corbis:** Paul Almsay 228 (*center*), Yann Arthus-Bertrand 246, Philip Bailey 149 (*top*), Roger Ball 173, Tom Bean 212, Lester V. Bergman 215 (*bottom*), Bettmann 209, 232, Clouds Hill Imaging Ltd. 215 (*top*), Bryn Colton/Assignment Photographers 184, Duomo 177, Kevin Fleming 226, Yves Forestier 214, Owen Franken 156, 159 (*bottom*), Eric & David Hosking 242 (*bottom*), John Hulme/Eye Ubiquitous 228 (*top*), Jacqui Hurst 153, Chuck Keeler Jr. 252, Lester Lefkowitz 216 (*top*), John Maher 251, Tom & Dee Ann McCarthy 187, George McCarthy 195, Mark Peterson 250, Roger Ressmeyer 238, Stephane Ruet/Corbis Sygma 249, Sakamoto Photo Research Laboratory 242 (*top*), Paul A. Souders 201, Michael S. Yamashita 186, Yogi Inc. 253; **DaimlerChrysler:** 140 (*top*), 142 (*top right*), 142 (*bottom left*), 143, 145 (*top*), 145 (*bottom*), 149 (*bottom*), 175, 221 (*left*), 221 (*center*), 221 (*right*); **Digital Vision:** 135 (*bottom left*), 203; **Ecoscene:** Ian Harwood 169; **Ford Motor Company:** 146;

Getty Images: 154 (*top*), 225, 234, 235; **Hemera Photo Objects:** 158, 168; **NASA:** 132, 133, 134, 135 (*top right*), 198; **National Library of Medicine:** 167; **Newscast:** Corus 200; **NHPA:** Kevin Schafer 180 (*top*), 196; **PA Photos:** 164, 247; **PHIL:** 152, 154 (*bottom*); **Photodisc:** 178, 185, 183 (*left*), 185, 188, 190 (*bottom*), 191, 192, 193 (*top*), 193 (*bottom*), 233, 240, 241; **Rex Features:** 194, 218, 220, 227, 230, 236, 239; **Robert Hunt Library:** 207; **Salter:** 159 (*top*); **Science Photo Library:** 197, Dr. Tony Brain 155, Montreal Neurological Institute/McGill University/CNRI 216 (*bottom*), Michel Viard/Peter Arnold Inc. 161; **Science & Society Picture Library:** Science Museum 163, 150, 151; **Still Pictures:** Fritz Polking 180 (*bottom*), Mark Edwards 183 (*right*); **Topham Picturepoint:** 204, 219, Image Works 160, 165, 166; **University of Pennsylvania Library:** Smith Collection 138, 170; **USDA/ARS:** Scott Bauer 229, Jack Dykinga 221, 213, Keith Weller 179, 210; **U.S. Dept. of Defense:** 206, 208; **U.S. Library of Congress:** 141 (*top*), 141 (*center*); **Volkswagen:** 140 (*bottom*)

CONTENTS

KEY TO COLOR CODING OF ARTICLES

EARTH, SPACE, AND ENVIRONMENTAL SCIENCES

PHYSICS AND CHEMISTRY

LIFE SCIENCES AND MEDICINE

TECHNOLOGY

MATHEMATICS

PEOPLE

Atmosphere

Earth is surrounded by a blanket of gaseous chemicals called the atmosphere. Without the atmosphere, life on Earth could not survive. The atmosphere provides life-supporting oxygen and contains water vapor, which falls as rain. The atmosphere also protects us from harmful radiation in sunlight and the dangerous threat of meteors.

Earth is thought to have formed about five billion years ago. During the first 500 million years, a dense atmosphere emerged from the vapor and gases expelled from the developing planet's interior. These consisted of water vapor (H_2O), hydrogen (H_2), methane (CH_4), carbon dioxide (CO_2), and carbon monoxide (CO). Around four billion years ago, water began to settle on Earth's surface. By this time, the atmosphere consisted largely of carbon dioxide, carbon monoxide, water, nitrogen (N_2), and hydrogen.

Early life

Around one billion years ago, microscopic life-forms called cyanobacteria began to use energy from the Sun to make food and oxygen gas (O_2) from molecules of water and carbon dioxide gas. Gradually, oxygen levels in the atmosphere increased while the level of carbon dioxide decreased.

The ozone layer

High in the atmosphere, some of the oxygen gas absorbed energy from the Sun's ultraviolet (UV) rays and split to form single oxygen atoms (O). These atoms combined with oxygen gas to form ozone (O_3) molecules. Ozone is very effective at absorbing UV rays. At first, the amount of UV radiation reaching Earth's surface was very high. Life was restricted to the oceans. By around 600 million years ago, however, an ozone layer had developed that was thick enough to protect life on land.

Present-day atmosphere

Today, there are five distinct layers in Earth's atmosphere. The nearest layer to Earth's surface is the troposphere. Then comes the stratosphere, mesosphere, thermosphere, and finally the exosphere, farthest away from Earth's surface. Each layer is separated by thin transition zones. Scientists do not know exactly how and why these layers formed. The amounts of gases found in each layer differ. Due to the effects of gravity, 99 percent of all the atmospheric gases is concentrated in the first 25 miles (40 kilometers) above Earth's surface. Despite the atmosphere's importance, it is remarkably thin in relation to the circumference of Earth. On average, the atmosphere's gases extend 600 miles (960 kilometers) out into space. This sounds like a lot, but if Earth were the size of a party balloon, the atmosphere would be no thicker than the balloon's rubber skin.

The troposphere

The lowest layer in the atmosphere is called the troposphere. Virtually

◀ *Seen from space, Earth is covered with swirling clouds of water vapor. These clouds, and most of the weather, occur in the lowest level of the atmosphere, called the troposphere.*

DID YOU KNOW?

The atmosphere controls the temperature on Earth. It absorbs most of the incoming radiation (light) from the Sun. However, some solar radiation does penetrate the atmosphere. It is reflected back as infrared radiation (heat), which is also absorbed by the atmosphere to heat our planet. Without the atmosphere, the heat would be lost, and Earth would be much cooler than it is. Atmospheric heat influences the weather in many ways, including air currents, local temperature, and rainfall.

▶ *The atmosphere is made up of five layers: the troposphere, stratosphere, mesosphere, thermosphere, and exosphere. The tropopause splits the troposphere from the stratosphere; the stratopause divides the stratosphere and mesosphere; the mesopause divides the mesosphere from the thermosphere; and the thermopause divides the thermosphere from the exosphere.*

▼ *The Moon rises above the blue glow of Earth's atmosphere. The atmosphere acts like a protective blanket. Without it, nothing could survive on Earth.*

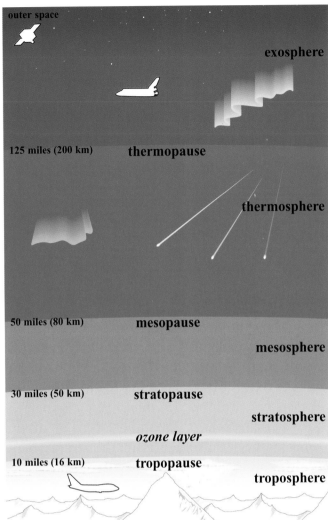

outer space

exosphere

125 miles (200 km) thermopause

thermosphere

50 miles (80 km) mesopause

mesosphere

30 miles (50 km) stratopause

stratosphere

ozone layer

10 miles (16 km) tropopause

troposphere

all of the planet's weather occurs in this layer of Earth's atmosphere. The troposphere extends to between 5 and 10 miles (8 and 16 kilometers) above Earth's surface. The troposphere is about 78 percent nitrogen, 21 percent oxygen, 0.9 percent argon, and 0.037 percent carbon dioxide. It also contains traces of water vapor and other gases, including helium, hydrogen, krypton, neon, and ozone.

In the troposphere, temperature and levels of water vapor decrease rapidly with altitude. On average, the temperature falls by 3.5°F every 1,000 feet (6.4°C every 1,000 meters). At the upper boundary of the troposphere, however, the temperature stops decreasing with altitude. This is the transition zone called the tropopause. Temperatures here can drop to −70°F (−58°F).

The stratosphere

The next major layer, the stratosphere, extends up to about 30 miles (50 kilometers) above Earth's surface. Temperatures slowly increase again to 28°F (12°C). The ozone layer is located in the stratosphere, around 15 miles (24 kilometers) above Earth's surface. Around 90 percent of the ozone in the atmosphere is in the stratosphere. Weather conditions strongly affect its distribution.

The stratopause and mesosphere

The upper limit of the stratosphere is marked by the stratopause, where temperatures stop increasing. Above this lies the next atmospheric

▲ This picture of Earth was taken from space. The bright glow is called the northern lights. It is caused by tiny particles interacting with the atmosphere.

layer, the mesosphere. With increasing distance from the surface, the atmosphere becomes enriched with lighter gases. Concentrations of ozone and water vapor in the mesosphere drop to almost zero, so temperatures decrease again, falling to as low as −130°F (−90°C) at the mesosphere's upper boundary. This is marked by the mesopause, where temperatures stop decreasing. It occurs about 50 miles (80 kilometers) above Earth's surface.

The thermosphere

In the next layer, the thermosphere, temperatures rise dramatically, reaching up to 2700°F (1480°C). The Sun's rays pass into the thermosphere and break the layer's molecules into positive ions and negative electrons. These ions and electrons reflect radiowaves from Earth back toward the surface, enabling the reception of long-range radio broadcasts. The thermosphere also protects us from objects in space, such as meteors. Gases in the thermosphere create friction as debris falls toward Earth, so it gradually burns away. The thermosphere extends up to around 125 miles (200 kilometers) above Earth's surface. The major components of the atmosphere at this level are nitrogen and oxygen, but at this extreme height, gas molecules are few and far between.

> **DID YOU KNOW?**
>
> Other planets, and several moons of these planets, also have atmospheres. Each of these atmospheres is unique, but they all follow the same scientific laws as our own. Life cannot survive in the atmospheres of the other planets in the solar system. No planets have life-supporting water in the atmosphere, the surface temperatures are either too hot or too cold, and their atmospheres do not have enough oxygen to support complex life or an ozone layer to filter out harmful UV radiation.

The exosphere

The final layer is the exosphere—the barrier between Earth and space. Its upper boundary is thought to reach as high as 620 miles (1,000 kilometers). Temperatures here range from about 570°F (300°C) to more than 3000°F (1650°C). Gases are present only in very small quantities.

Atmospheric pollution

There is growing concern over the impact of humans on the atmosphere. Human activities may be increasing levels of heat-absorbing gases, so causing global warming and destroying ozone. Other artificial emissions contaminate the air with toxic gases and create acid rain.

Heat-absorbing greenhouse gases include carbon dioxide, nitrous oxide (N_2O), and methane. Some of these gases escape naturally from living and dead organisms. These gases are also produced by burning fossil fuels such as coal. Greenhouse gases prevent heat from escaping from Earth and create the warming greenhouse effect. Greenhouse gas emissions from human activities are increasing the greenhouse effect and causing global warming.

Ozone holes and acid rain

The true effect of human activities on the ozone layer is still unclear. It is known that ozone levels change as part of regular natural cycles, such as seasons, and also because of events such as volcanic eruptions. Measurements taken over the last 50 years, however, have shown that there has been a steady depletion of ozone. Holes have appeared in the ozone layer over the Arctic

◀ Many power stations burn fossil fuels to generate electricity. The gases contained in the smoke enter the atmosphere and are known to cause acid rain.

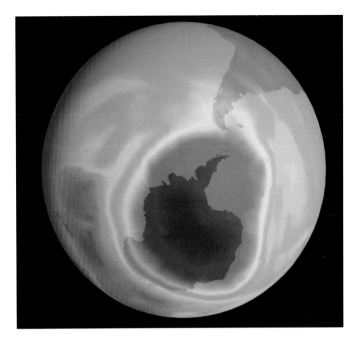

▲ This colored image of Earth shows the ozone hole (purple) over Antarctica. Ozone protects life from harmful UV radiation in sunlight.

and Antarctic. They are thought to be caused by human-made gases entering the atmosphere and destroying ozone. These gases include chlorofluorocarbons (CFCs) used in aerosols and cooling systems, and halons, used in fire extinguishers. Increasing efforts are now being made to limit the use of such damaging gases. Many countries have banned their use entirely.

Other artificial atmospheric pollutants are created by burning fossil fuels, incinerating garbage, and many industrial processes. These pollutants include nitrogen oxides, carbon monoxide, and sulfur oxides. These toxic compounds have a range of destructive effects on life on Earth. They can cause lung diseases and many other serious long-term health effects in people. Some pollutants can also create acid rain. Acid rain contains high levels of sulfuric acid (H_2SO_4) and nitric acid (HNO_3), picked up as a result of atmospheric pollution. Acid rain can contaminate drinking water, damage aquatic life, kill plants, and erode buildings.

See also: POLLUTION • RAIN AND RAINFALL

Atom and molecule

Everything in the universe consists of tiny particles called atoms. Atoms are the building blocks of matter. They consist of even smaller particles called protons, neutrons, and electrons. Protons and neutrons make up the dense nucleus at the center of an atom. Electrons revolve around the nucleus in a series of layers called electron shells. Atoms of different elements combine chemically to form particles called molecules.

All the physical and chemical properties of a substance depend on its atoms and the way they are arranged within that substance. Any substance made up from atoms all containing the same number of protons is called an element.

The number of protons in each atom is called the atomic number of the element. Atomic numbers range from 1 (hydrogen) to 112 (an as-yet unnamed element made by German scientists in 1996). For example, carbon has an atomic number of 6, while lead has an atomic number of 82.

Electricity and the atom

Subatomic particles—protons, neutrons, and electrons—have different electrical properties. Protons carry a tiny positive electrical charge. Electrons carry an equal but opposite (negative) charge. Neutrons have no charge at all. Stable atoms contain equal numbers of protons and electrons so the overall electrical charge is zero.

To give a substance an electrical charge, the balance of protons and electrons must change in some way. A simple way to do this is by means of friction. If you rub a balloon with a piece of silk, for example, electrons will transfer from the silk to the balloon, and the balloon will then carry a negative charge. The silk will carry more protons than electrons, so it will be positively charged.

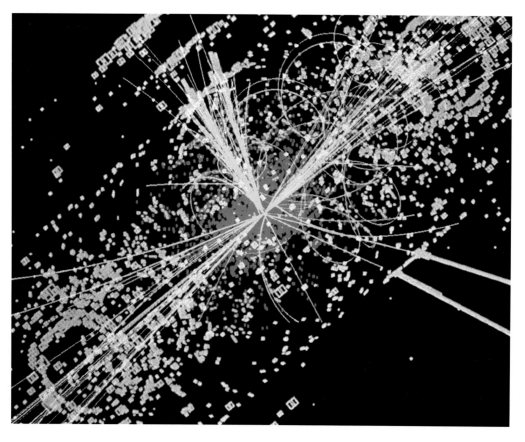

◀ *A computer simulation shows the results of a collision between a pair of high-energy protons at CERN—the European Organization for Nuclear Research. The yellow lines indicate the path of particles, called hadrons, produced as the protons collide. The collision also generates huge amounts of energy, shown in blue.*

One property of an electrically charged object is that it will attract an uncharged object. A feather or some other light object will cling to the surface of the charged balloon or silk until the balloon or the silk loses the charge.

Isotopes and atomic mass

The atoms of one element all contain the same number of protons, but the atoms may contain different numbers of neutrons. For example, most carbon atoms contain six neutrons, but about one percent of the atoms each contain seven neutrons. These different types of atom of the same element are called isotopes. The isotopes of an element all have the same chemical properties, but some of the physical properties, such as the melting point and boiling point, are different.

The atomic mass of an atom is the total number of protons and neutrons that it contains. (Electrons are so light and add so little to the mass of an atom that they can be ignored.) Scientists use the atomic mass to refer to a particular isotope. For example, the common natural isotope of carbon, which contains six protons and six neutrons, is called carbon-12. The rarer natural isotope, which contains an extra neutron, is called carbon-13.

Besides the natural isotopes, scientists can produce various artificial isotopes during nuclear reactions in the laboratory. These reactions involve changes in the dense nucleus at the center of an atom. The isotopes carbon-10, carbon-11, carbon-14, and carbon-15 can be produced in this way.

Atomic weight

The atomic mass of an element is always a whole number, but the atomic weight is not. The atomic weight is the average atomic mass of a known

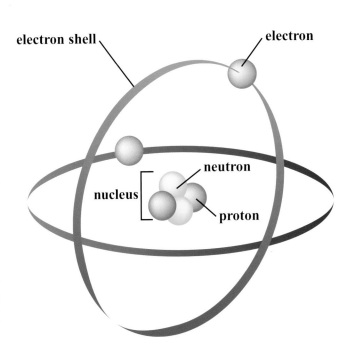

▲ *This diagram shows the structure of a helium atom. There are two positively charged protons and two uncharged neutrons in the dense nucleus at the center of the atom. Two negatively charged electrons revolve around the nucleus in two layers called electron shells.*

mixture of isotopes. Normally, this is the mixture that occurs in nature. For example, natural carbon is made up of 98.9 percent carbon-12 atoms, with the remainder being carbon-13 atoms. From these figures scientists can calculate that the atomic weight of carbon is 12.011.

Molecules and molecular weight

Atoms often occur in groups called molecules. A molecule of hydrogen gas, for example, consists of two hydrogen atoms joined by a chemical bond. Scientists represent the molecule by the chemical formula H_2. Similarly, a molecule of oxygen gas has the chemical formula O_2. This shows that the molecule contains two atoms of oxygen. Molecules that contain two atoms of the same element are called diatomic molecules.

The molecular weight of a substance is the sum of the atomic weights of all the atoms in one molecule. Since oxygen gas contains two oxygen atoms, the molecular weight of oxygen gas is double the atomic weight.

DID YOU KNOW?

Almost all naturally occurring elements have more than one stable isotope. The only exceptions are aluminum, beryllium, phosphorus, and sodium.

▲ *Ernest Rutherford was awarded the Nobel Prize for physics in 1908 for his investigations into the disintegration of elements and the chemistry of radioactive substances.*

Compounds

Elements, such as carbon, hydrogen, and oxygen, are simple substances. Compounds are more complex substances. Some molecules contain atoms of more than one element. For example, water is a compound made of the elements hydrogen and oxygen. One molecule of water contains two hydrogen atoms and one oxygen atom. Scientists represent this molecule by the chemical formula H_2O.

Most molecules of compounds are more complex. For example, one sulfuric acid molecule consists of two hydrogen atoms, one sulfur atom,

and four oxygen atoms. The formula for a molecule of sulfuric acid is written as H_2SO_4. Sulfuric acid is still a fairly simple compound compared with the giant protein molecules in the human body. Most protein molecules contain hundreds, or even thousands, of atoms and have molecular weights ranging up to about ten million. However, they are still too small to be seen with the naked eye.

Solids, liquids, and gases

Molecules are always moving. The molecules in solid substances pack together tightly, and they vibrate about fixed points. Strong forces of attraction between the molecules prevent them from moving past each other. Because of this attraction, a solid object tends to keep its shape.

Most solids can be changed into liquids by heating. Heating a substance makes the molecules in the substance move faster. Eventually, they are able to move past each other into new positions. As a result, a solid substance can change its shape and flow readily. The solid then changes into a liquid. This process is called melting.

Further heating makes the molecules of a liquid substance move even faster. When the liquid reaches its boiling point, some molecules have enough energy to break through the surface of the liquid and escape. The liquid then changes into a gas. This process is called evaporation.

Pressure can also make substances change from one physical state to another. Some gases turn into liquids when their molecules squeeze together due to an increase in pressure. Gas fuel for a camping stove is stored as a liquid in a high-pressure cylinder. Opening a valve in the cylinder reduces the pressure, and the fuel comes out as a gas.

Inside the atom

By the end of the nineteenth century, scientists knew a lot about the behavior of atoms. They knew less about atomic structure, because atoms were too small to see, even using powerful microscopes.

Electrical experiments had provided a vital clue about the structure of atoms. A high voltage was found to produce invisible rays streaming between

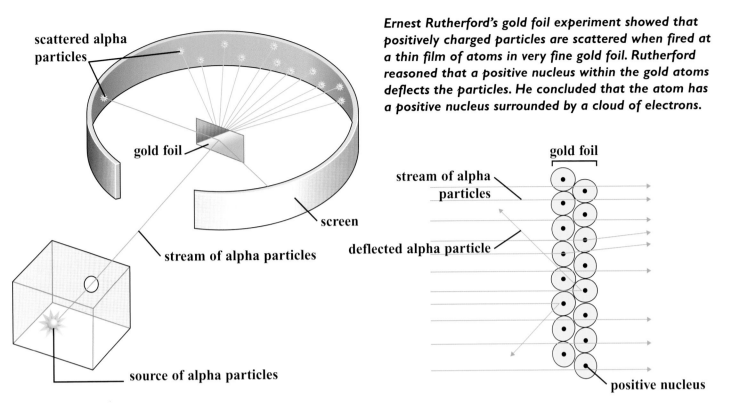

scattered alpha particles

gold foil

stream of alpha particles

screen

source of alpha particles

Ernest Rutherford's gold foil experiment showed that positively charged particles are scattered when fired at a thin film of atoms in very fine gold foil. Rutherford reasoned that a positive nucleus within the gold atoms deflects the particles. He concluded that the atom has a positive nucleus surrounded by a cloud of electrons.

gold foil

stream of alpha particles

deflected alpha particle

positive nucleus

two metal plates in an empty, sealed tube. British physicist J. J. Thomson (1856–1940) showed that the invisible rays consisted of negatively charged particles. Thomson called these particles "corpuscles," but Dutch physicist Hendrik Lorentz (1853–1928) later called them electrons. Thomson assumed correctly that the electrons came from the atoms of the metal plate emitting the invisible rays. Just exactly how the electrons were arranged within an atom remained a mystery, however.

In 1911, New Zealand–born British physicist Ernest Rutherford (1871–1937), who had studied with Thomson, put forward his model of atomic structure. Rutherford fired positively charged alpha particles at a thin piece of gold foil (see the diagram above). Rutherford suggested that the atom resembled a miniature solar system. Electrons orbit (revolve around) a positive nucleus in the same way as planets orbit the Sun. Rutherford's explanation is perfectly satisfactory for most purposes, but the structure of the atom is really more complicated. A few years after Rutherford announced his model, Danish physicist Niels Bohr (1885–1962) showed that electrons orbit only at certain distances from the nucleus. In Bohr's model of the atom, the

nucleus has a series of invisible "shells" around it. The electrons orbit only in the shells, but they sometimes jump from one shell to another.

How many particles?

In 1932, British physicist James Chadwick (1891–1974) discovered a particle called the neutron that had no electrical charge. Scientists suspected that other particles produce the forces that hold protons and neutrons together in the nucleus. These binding particles, called mesons, prompted the search for new subatomic particles.

Physicists now probe the atom with powerful machines called particle accelerators. The result has been the discovery of many different subatomic particles, from quarks and neutrinos to gluons and muons. Scientists now plan to build a particle accelerator to recreate the conditions of the big bang, which they hope will reveal new ideas about the particles and forces that have shaped our world.

See also: BOHR, NIELS • PARTICLE ACCELERATOR • PARTICLE DETECTOR • PARTICLE PHYSICS • RUTHERFORD, ERNEST

Automobile

The automobile is one of the most important inventions of all time. It has become the most common means of transportation, and it allows people to travel almost anywhere in comfort. Every year in the United States alone, twice as many cars are built as babies are born.

The first automobile driven by a gasoline engine appeared in the late nineteenth century, but people had been trying to build steam-driven cars for many years before that. The first person to sit behind the controls of a self-propelled car was French engineer Nicolas Cugnot (1725–1804). In 1770, Cugnot built a three-wheeled, steam-powered machine that could reach a top speed of 6 miles per hour (10 kilometers per hour).

However, steam was not an effective means of powering automobiles. Steam engines need a boiler and a large water tank, as well as an engine and fuel for the fire. Engineers also looked to design electric cars in the late nineteenth century. But the batteries of the time were too heavy and they did not last long enough with one charge.

Modern cars come in all shapes and sizes, from the angular profile of the BMW 3-series (middle) to the sleek curves of the Volkswagen Beetle (bottom). Overcrowded cities have made smaller cars, such as MCC's Smart car (top), very popular.

Henry Ford revolutionized the automobile industry and manufacturing in general when he introduced mass production to his factories. His low-priced Model T Ford made automobile ownership affordable for most people and changed transportation forever.

The car before 1900

In 1876, a German engineer, Nikolaus Otto (1832–1891), invented an internal combustion engine powered by gasoline. Following in Otto's footsteps were two more fine German engineers, Karl Benz (1844–1929) and Gottlieb Daimler (1834–1900). Benz and Daimler independently built the world's first cars fitted with internal combustion engines. The Benz of 1885 was a three-wheeled car with an open, wooden two-seater body. The vehicle had one wheel at the front, which was steered by a tiller. The two large rear wheels were driven by chains, which were turned by a single-cylinder gasoline engine. The engine produced about ½ horsepower and drove the car at a top speed of 10 miles per hour (16 kilometers per hour). Daimler's car was a converted carriage with four wheels. It had a single-cylinder engine that produced 1½ horsepower.

By 1900, various automobile designs had appeared. Inventions included the carburetor, the steering wheel (levers were used before), the pneumatic tire, engines with more than one cylinder, the gate gearchange, and the radiator.

The first motor race was held in 1895, from Paris to Bordeaux in France. The drivers traveled a distance of 750 miles (1,200 kilometers), and the race was won by a 4-horsepower, twin-cylinder car made by French engineers René Panhard (1841–1908) and Émile Lavassor (1844–1897). The winners took 48 hours; Lavassor, who was driving the car, averaged 15 miles (24 kilometers) per hour, even though he fell asleep at the wheel on the return to Paris.

Many U.S. engineers also experimented with gasoline-powered vehicles. Among them were brothers Charles Duryea (1861–1938) and Frank Duryea (1870–1967), who built the first successful U.S. gasoline-powered automobile in 1893.

The automobile between 1900 and 1920

In the early 1900s, automobile designers created more powerful engines, which resulted in faster road speeds. Cars then required better brakes and transmission systems. The early brakes were the same as those used on bicycles and carriages: a solid block of wood, leather, or metal pressed against the wheel rims when the driver operated a hand lever. Then came brake drums, in which a band of material closes on drums attached to the wheels.

There were two other important changes in the early twentieth century. The price of gasoline dropped sharply after the discovery of rich oil fields in Texas. Then, mass production of automobiles began in the Unites States. In 1908, the first Model T Ford, designed by U.S. engineer Henry Ford (1863–1947), rolled off the production line. By 1911, Ford's factories were producing 1,000 automobiles a day. Over the next 19 years, more than 15 million

Model T Fords were made. General Motors started up in 1908 when U.S. automobile manufacturers Buick, Cadillac, Oakland, and Oldsmobile joined forces. General Motors immediately became the world's biggest car manufacturer.

1920 to today

Between World War I (1914–1918) and World War II (1939–1945), the mass production of automobiles became well established. There was a wide range of cheap, reliable, and comfortable vehicles. Engines became more efficient and powerful. Other improvements included four-wheel brakes, windshield wipers, shatterproof glass, independent suspension, and grooved tires. In 1937, General Motors produced an affordable automatic transmission. U.S. manufacturers began to make powerful luxury automobiles. In Europe, manufacturers turned to small, low-priced cars such as the British Austin 7, the Italian Fiat 500, and the German Volkswagen.

After World War II, automobiles became longer, lower, and more elaborate. Curved glass was used to make the windshields. Chromium plating became popular. The tubeless tire was developed in 1948. Power steering and disc brakes were introduced in the early 1950s. In addition to these improvements, manufacturers worked to develop more powerful engines that enabled cars to go faster.

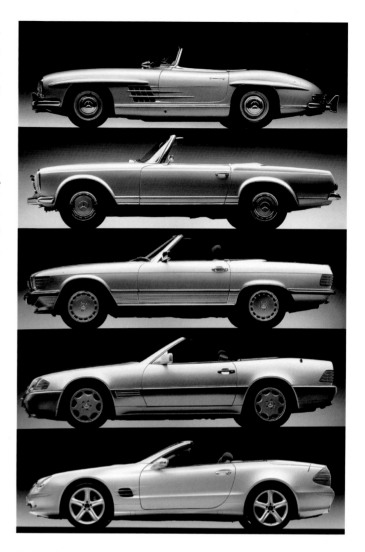

▲ As the years have passed, cars have not only gotten faster, but their designs have changed. These pictures show five generations of the SL-class Mercedes Roadster, starting with the oldest at the top.

CAR COMPONENTS

There are many differences in automobile design, but a typical model has an engine at the front to drive the back wheels as well as suspension, brake, and steering systems.

The engine

The engine is the heart of the car. Modern automobile engines are highly efficient machines that convert liquid gasoline into energy that turns

◀ Almost all cars are now made on production lines. Robots do much of the work, but skilled people are still required to work on the vehicles at various stages before they leave the factory.

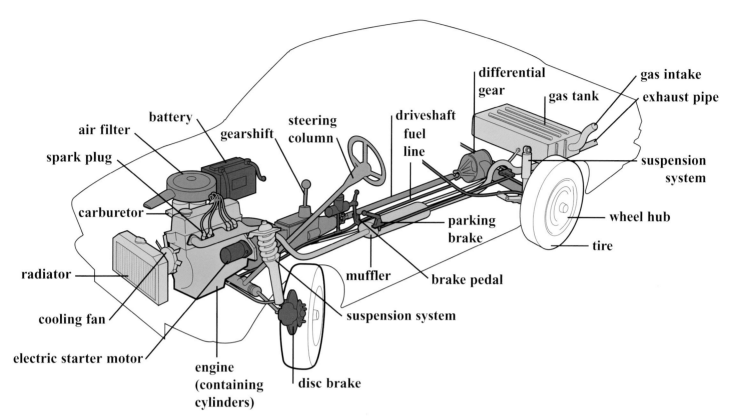

air filter

spark plug

carburetor

radiator

cooling fan

electric starter motor

battery

gearshift

steering column

driveshaft fuel line

differential gear

gas tank

gas intake

exhaust pipe

suspension system

wheel hub

tire

parking brake

muffler

brake pedal

suspension system

engine (containing cylinders)

disc brake

▲ *This diagram shows all of the essential working parts of a typical car. The transmission system takes power from the engine to the rear, or driving, wheels.*

▶ *The engine is a car's powerhouse. Most cars have the engine mounted at the front, although in a few models, the engine is mounted at the back of the vehicle.*

the wheels. A fuel pump driven by the engine draws gasoline from the tank. The gasoline then passes to the carburetor, where mixes with air. The amount of gas-air mixture supplied to the engine depends on how far the driver presses the gas pedal.

The gas–air mixture is fed to each of the engine's cylinders through the inlet valves. As the piston in a cylinder rises, the inlet valves close and the mixture is compressed. An electrical spark from a spark plug at the top of the cylinder explodes the mixture.

This explosion forces the piston down the cylinder. On its return up the cylinder, the piston pushes out the burned gases. They pass out of the cylinder through an exhaust valve, which opens at just the right moment, and are expelled from the vehicle through the exhaust pipe.

Each of the automobile's pistons drives a connecting rod. The connecting rods are joined to the crankshaft and turn the up-and-down movements of the pistons into the rotary movement of the crankshaft. At the end of the crankshaft is a heavy flywheel that keeps the engine running smoothly.

Getting power to the wheels

It takes a lot of power to move an automobile. The transmission (gear system) passes the power from the engine to the driveshaft, which turns the wheels. The transmission can reduce the speed to increase the turning power or reduce the turning power to increase the speed. To set a car in motion or push it up a hill, the transmission gives less speed and more turning power to the driveshaft. When the automobile is cruising along a level highway, the transmission provides more speed and less turning power to the driveshaft.

With automatic transmission, the speed of the driveshaft is chosen automatically. With a manual transmission, the driver engages the gears using a gearshift lever and a clutch pedal. The driver first pushes his or her foot down on the clutch pedal, then shifts the lever to first gear to move off, then into higher gears as the automobile gains speed. Most cars now have five gears. The driver can also use a reverse gear for going backward. The driver must operate the clutch for each gear change to disconnect the engine from the transmission.

The driveshaft is a steel rod that takes the power from the transmission back to the differential through universal joints. Universal joints are made so that the rear axles can bump up and down without breaking the driveshaft. The differential is a set of gears that allows the two separate shafts turning the back wheels to turn at different speeds. The outside wheel of a cornering vehicle goes more quickly than the wheel on the inside of the corner.

The suspension

To make the automobile comfortable to ride in, the wheels are attached to the body by a suspension system. There are several types of suspension, but in most cars, springs and shock absorbers are used.

Leaf springs consist of layers of flexible material shaped like a bow. Each end of the bow is connected to the chassis of the automobile, while the center is joined to the axle. Coil springs are strong springs that connect directly between the axle and the chassis. Shock absorbers in the springing system cut down the up-and-down movement of the springs to stop bouncing.

The brakes

On each of the four wheels is a brake drum or disc brake. When the driver presses on the brake pedal, a pair of brake shoes expands and rubs against the inside of the drum. In the case of the disc brake, pads squeeze the disc between them. Both shoes and pads are made of high friction material that slows the wheels.

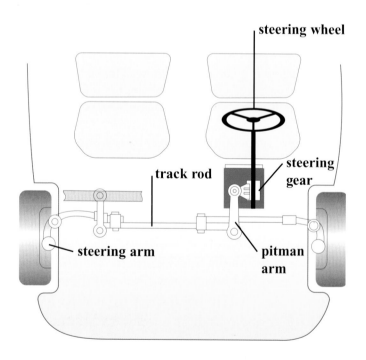

▲ *When the driver turns the steering wheel, the pitman arm moves the track rod left or right. This pushes the back of one wheel and pulls the other wheel so that both the wheels move in the same direction.*

◀ *Satellite technology has led to the development of in-car navigation systems that advise the driver how best to get to his or her destination.*

Both kinds of brakes work by hydraulic pressure. When the driver presses the brake pedal, liquid is forced out of a master cylinder into brake cylinders at each wheel. The brake cylinders work the brake shoes and pads.

The steering mechanism

A typical automobile is steered by the front wheels. The steering wheel turns a shaft that connects at its bottom end to steering gears. These gears move rods that are pulled to the left or right and move the wheels. Some cars have hydraulic power steering to make turning the steering wheel much easier.

The ignition and cooling systems

The spark produced by the spark plug must be very accurately timed, and this is the job of the ignition system. Electric current produced by the car battery passes to the distributor, which gives a short burst of current at the exact moment needed for ignition at each cylinder.

A machine that works by a series of explosions gets very hot. Most engines are cooled by water. A pump forces water around the cylinder block and through a radiator to get rid of unwanted heat. Behind the radiator is a fan that draws air through the radiator. Both the fan and the water pump are driven by a belt from the crankshaft.

▶ *Some cars have headlight washers. These ensure that the headlight beam travels as far as possible, so the driver can better see the road ahead.*

CAR SAFETY

Even from the early days, when cars traveled relatively slowly, the need for car safety has been very important. Designers and engineers are always looking to prevent accidents and lessen the injuries when accidents do happen.

Active safety measures aim to reduce the chances of a car being involved in an accident in the first place. They are concerned with road holding, stability, and visibility, and involve the brakes, lights, tires, and all the controls that make it easier to drive the

car. Passive safety measures assume that some accidents will always happen, and aim to reduce the effects of accidents and the number of serious injuries. Seat belts are an example of passive safety. Airbags are another development in this area.

Improvements in design

New rubber compounds have been introduced that help reduce the possibility of the tires skidding. Some tires still run for a limited distance after a flat or puncture without suffering damage or rolling off the wheel rim. General features, such as better steering mechanisms, wing mirrors, multispeed window wipers, and washers give the driver clear views of the road in front and behind. These features also help make driving safer.

Brake safety

Many modern cars have disc brakes rather than drum brakes. When drum brakes are used too often, they heat up, expand, and do not work so well. Disc brakes do not have this problem because friction pads press against a disc on the axle and still work when the disc heats up.

▼ Before a new model of car goes on sale, it must pass a crash-dummy test. Safety testing such as this allows the manufacturer to put the car through its paces and make sure that it is safe to drive.

Research into safety

Dummies strapped into car seats are used to find out what happens in a high-speed crash and what difference airbags, antiburst door locks, head rests, safety glass, seat belts, and other safety features are likely to make. Modern cars have "crumple zones" at the front and back. Crumple zones fold up if the car is involved in a collision. They reduce the impact, while the center of the car, where the passengers sit, remains more intact. Making sure that the car is free of sharp projections further reduces the chances of injury.

Using seat belts

The laws governing seat belt use vary across the United States. Some states insist only on small children having specially fitted seats and belts or harnesses for protection. Road safety experts estimate that if everyone wore seat belts, more than half of all the injuries and fatalities suffered in road traffic accidents could be avoided.

Seat belts hold the driver and his or her passengers firmly in their seats, while the car itself absorbs the impact of the crash. Even when the car is skidding, it is more likely that a driver wearing a seat belt will be able to regain control and avoid a crash. Some simple seat belts have to be tight all the time. Most belts, however, allow movement during

1978
KPW-11326

normal driving but lock into place during a crash. They must be adjusted so that the load falls across the pelvis and chest, otherwise the seat belt may cause injuries in a crash.

Preventing accidents

Modern cars have many other safety measures. Antiburst door locks hold the door closed in a crash to stop people from being thrown out. An energy-absorbing steering wheel column keeps the steering wheel from smashing into the driver's chest. Head rests help prevent neck injuries. Laminated safety glass in windshields reduces the chance of such injuries as deep cuts in the face. It also helps prevent occupants being thrown out of the car. Laminated glass is made of two sheets of glass separated by a layer of transparent plastic, and does not shatter like normal glass.

Protecting pedestrians

When cars crash, pedestrians are at risk. In fact, as many pedestrians are killed as drivers each year in the United States. Some countries have passed laws that restrict the fitting of sharp or dangerous items, such as hood ornaments, on the front and sides of cars. This reduces the chance of serious cuts if a car does hit a pedestrian.

By setting the bumper or fender height on the low side, and arranging for the front of the car to slope smoothly away, designers with safety in mind reduce the risk of injury. If a car does hit a pedestrian, then the person is likely to be thrown up and out of the way rather than be dragged underneath the car.

RACE CARS

Motor racing is a sport that has thrilled millions since it began in 1895. It now takes many forms, from Grand Prix racing to rallying. However, there is more to racing than entertainment. Racing car design helps engineers understand and solve all kinds of mechanical problems.

The first automobiles were fragile and unreliable machines. They traveled slowly and regularly broke down. The first proper road race was held in 1895

DID YOU KNOW?

The fastest cars are those designed specifically to break land speed records. The current official land speed record was set by British fighter pilot Andy Green in 1997. Green broke the sound barrier in the jet-engined supersonic *Thrust SSC*, which reached a speed of 763 miles per hour (1,228 kilometers per hour).

between Paris and Bordeaux in France. The winners averaged a speed of only 15 miles per hour (24 kilometers per hour). Today, racing cars reach speeds well in excess of 200 miles per hour (322 kilometers per hour). The huge technological advances made in the automobile industry in the space of just one hundred years owe much to the sport of motor racing.

Motor racing has been through many changes in its short history. The first races were often run from one town to the next along the public highway. One race was even run from Paris to Peking. Concern for safety, however, ensured that motor racing soon only took place on race tracks. Racing remains a dangerous sport, however, and many famous drivers have lost their lives. Designers must think of safety as much as speed when building a race car.

Formula One racing

International long-distance racing began in France in 1906, although for the previous six years a U.S. publisher sponsored the annual international event known as the Gordon Bennett Cup. Ever since World War I (1914–1918), each European nation has held its own Grand Prix event in which drivers from all over the world compete.

The United States took a slightly different direction. Oval dirt tracks, originally laid down for horse racing, were used for motor racing. As the speed of cars increased, oval tracks with banked corners were built. Races are still held on oval tracks in the United States. The most famous track is the 2½-mile (4-kilometer) Indianapolis Speedway.

In Europe the golden age of motor racing was the 1930s. The Grand Prix races encouraged fierce competition among car manufacturers. After World War II (1939–1945), the Grand Prix class of racing cars were called Formula One. The European competitions became truly international races. The first world champion was Italian Giuseppe Farina, who won in 1950.

The following years saw the rise of car manufacturers in Britain, France, and Italy as leading race car designers. The appearance of Formula One cars began to change. Engines at the rear did away with the heavy driveshaft, and the driver laid back in the cockpit seat. The front of the car became sleek and narrow so the air slipped freely over the car's body. Streamlining became all important. In 1962, British engineer Colin Chapman, then working at Lotus, brought out the monocoque (single-shell) combined chassis and body, using a very tough steel-reinforced aluminum alloy. In 1967, Italian car manufacturer Ferrari introduced airfoils—wings that force the car downward to grip the track. Tires became very wide to grip the surface. A modern racing tire is tubeless, lightweight, and driven at low pressure to avoid blowouts. Dry weather tires have no treads.

The most powerful Formula One cars were those from the 1980s, when turbochargers on engines were permitted. Current rules do not allow these devices. More recently, a whole array of electronic systems have been developed to make Formula One cars faster and easier to drive. Semi-automatic gearboxes and traction control, active suspension, and antilock brake systems all have their origins in Formula One. Many of the systems that are developed have been banned to try to maintain the importance of driver skill, but much of the technology later finds its way into road cars.

Sports car racing

Some of the best racing to watch is at sports car events. Two- or four-seater sports cars, classed as GT (Gran Turismo), are designed for high performance and endurance. GT sports cars are meant to be cars in general production, but there are also special classes for prototypes (models still at the design stage). In fact, some sports cars are almost as powerful as Formula One cars, and some builders of Grand Prix cars also produce sports cars. The world's most famous GT race is the 24-hour contest at Le Mans, France.

Other types of race car

The other classes of race cars include a great range of styles, each specially built but often including features from standard production models. These racers play an important part in automobile design and help drivers move up the racing ladder. Some of the most advanced of these classes are Formula 5000 and Formula Two.

New formulas or classes of race cars have been developed by the world's leading automobile firms. Formula Vee was started by Volkswagen in 1961, Ford UK set up Formula Ford, and Formule Renault was started by French car firm Renault. Many other manufacturers also now have their own race series.

Hot rods and drag racing

Hot-rod racing is an extremely popular sport in the United States. The race cars used are ordinary automobiles that have been modified for use on the race track. Sometimes the changes make the car suitable only for racing conditions, and it is illegal to drive them on the highway. Hot-rod racing has a history of illegal street racing. It is now controlled by the National Hot Rod Association (NHRA).

DID YOU KNOW?

Ever more complicated electronic systems are being used in modern cars. A car's computer is now almost as important as its engine. As well as controlling antilock braking systems, the computer can control the car's engine, adjusting engine timing and fueling for either power or economy. If wheel sensors detect wheelspin, it can also cut engine power to help traction control.

▲ *A jet engine provides maximum acceleration for this drag car. It uses parachutes to slow down.*

Drag racing developed from hot-rod racing and is a contest in acceleration. Cars are timed along a track known as a drag strip, which is only 440 yards (402 meters) long. The cars are specially built for this type of racing. The fastest dragsters can cover this distance in less than five seconds.

Stock-car racing

Every year about 10 million people watch stock-car racing in the United States. This popular sport does not use racing or sports cars but normal production models. There are different classes in which to compete based on the type of car and the amount of modification allowed.

▶ *Concept cars such as this F400 Mercedes Twisty Speedster give manufacturers a chance to test new ideas and hint at what cars might look like in years to come.*

The demolition derby is a lot of fun. In this competition, the drivers actually aim to smash into each other, while trying to avoid damage to themselves. Rollbars are placed inside the cars to make the structure stronger in case they roll over. Windshields are removed, and the drivers wear crash helmets and harnesses.

Rallying

Rallying is a sport in which specially modified cars are timed as they drive over public highways or trails. The driver travels from one control point to another and is helped by a passenger who acts as the navigator, planning the route and reading the maps. In some rallies, points are awarded for safe, legal driving. In others, drivers must battle against tough conditions, such as in the famous East African Safari Rally.

LOOKING TO THE FUTURE

It is likely that the gasoline-driven car will continue to be produced for many years to come. However, experiments are underway to find a cheaper fuel that will do less damage to the environment. Cars powered by electricity and hydrogen are being developed and may well be the cars of the future.

See also: ALTERNATIVE FUEL VEHICLE • BRAKE SYSTEM • DIESEL ENGINE • FUEL INJECTION • INTERNAL COMBUSTION ENGINE

Babbage, Charles

Charles Babbage was an English inventor and mathematician best known for his invention of analytical engines. These early calculating machines were an important step toward the development of the modern computer.

▲ Charles Babbage at the 1860 International Statistical Congress, London. In addition to the development of his calculating machines, Babbage wrote many important scientific papers.

Charles Babbage was born in Teignmouth, England, in 1791. He was the son of a wealthy banker and was educated first by private tutors and then at Cambridge University. In 1814, Babbage married and moved to London.

At that time, British mathematicians took little notice of developments in other countries. They concentrated on the theories of British scientist Isaac Newton (1642–1727) and ignored important work being done in the rest of Europe. With other scholars, Babbage founded the Analytical Society in 1812. This introduced British mathematicians to the ideas of people such as Gottfried Liebniz (1646–1716), Sylvestre Lacroix (1765–1843), and Leonhard Euler (1707–1783). Together with English astronomer John Herschel (1792–1871), Babbage translated Lacroix's work on calculus and wrote *Examples to the Differential and Integral Calculus*.

In Babbage's time, most calculations were done entirely by hand, although logarithm tables and a device similar to the slide rule were available. Even the various tables for accurate mathematics, astronomy, and navigation were all calculated laboriously by hand, a process that was lengthy and easily resulted in mistakes.

Babbage lived during a period of enormous technological progress. Industries were beginning to use machines, such as steam engines, but these were usually controlled by human operators and there was little automation. Babbage thought it should be possible to build machines to do calculations automatically.

Difference engines

In 1822, Babbage built a mechanical calculator that could perform simple calculations up to eight decimal places. In 1823, he was given a grant by the British government to design and build a machine to calculate mathematical tables. The machine would be accurate to 20 decimal places and would also automatically set the type for printing the tables. Babbage designed various machines and called them difference engines.

The work was due to be completed in 1827, but it was continually delayed. Babbage suffered a nervous breakdown when rumors spread that he had kept the grant money for personal use. In 1834, a skilled assistant resigned after having an argument with Babbage. The project collapsed, and Babbage's difference engines were never finished.

There was one major difficulty with Babbage's projects. Although his ideas and designs were brilliant, the technology needed to build many of the machines—the materials and the high-precision engineering techniques—did not yet exist. So Babbage's talent could be appreciated only long after his death in 1871.

Analytical engines

From 1835, Babbage worked on more advanced machines, which he called analytical engines. The analytical engines were designed to perform different calculations according to instructions fed in on a punched card. Babbage's associate, English mathematician Augusta Ada King, Countess of Lovelace (1815–1852), became an expert in creating the instructions on the punched cards. The analytical engines also had memories in which to store the results of calculations.

The analytical engines Babbage designed were never built during his lifetime. However, the concepts Babbage developed laid the foundations for the design of the modern computer more than one hundred years later. Countess Lovelace is credited with being the world's first computer programmer in recognition of her contribution.

A man of many talents

Babbage was active in many other fields of science. He wrote about geology, physics, and statistics, and he developed theories about mathematical code breaking. Babbage invented the heliograph—a device that uses sunlight and mirrors to send signals—and also the opthalmoscope, which physicians still use to look inside the eye.

See also: CALCULATOR • COMPUTER

◀ *One of Babbage's greatest achievements was the design of his analytical engines. These machines were so complex that none were ever completed during Babbage's lifetime. This is a replica that was built after his death.*

Bacteria

Bacteria are all around us—in the air we breathe, the food we eat, and the water we drink. Many of these tiny, single-celled organisms survive in Earth's extreme environments. They have been found in the depths of the oceans and high in the atmosphere. There are billions inside the human body. Some bacteria are harmful and cause diseases, but others are vital to the health of all living organisms.

Many people are quick to blame bacteria (*singular,* bacterium) for the damage they do and the infections they cause. However, only some bacteria cause disease. Most bacteria are useful, or at least harmless, to people. Some are responsible for breaking down dead animal and plant matter. Others turn nitrogen in the atmosphere into organic molecules, keeping the soil fertile. Scientists called bacteriologists study bacteria to discover their useful properties. Using genetic engineering, scientists are now looking for ways of changing bacteria to bring people even greater benefits.

Bacteria at work

When a plant or animal dies, bacteria break down the dead matter into simple chemicals that can be used by living things. This process is called decomposition or decay. It is most important in the soil, where bacteria make nitrogen from decaying matter.

Other bacteria take nitrogen from the air and change it into a form that can be used by plants. This process is called nitrogen fixation. Green plants must have nitrogen to grow. Animals depend on plant life, so animals depend on bacteria, too.

Scientists are now finding new ways of making bacteria useful in breaking down other unwanted material. Some bacteria attack naturally occurring hydrocarbons such as oil. The bacteria that are best at this job are selected and grown in vast quantities. They can then be used to help mop up oil spills. Bacteria were used in this way following the huge Exxon *Valdez* oil spill in Alaska in 1989. The oil cleanup following the 1991 Gulf War also was achieved in part using bacteria.

A variety of bacteria can be used to improve the environment. Scientists are working on mixtures of bacteria that will break down pesticides and weed killers. This might prevent these chemicals from getting into domestic water supplies. Some bacteria can produce polymers (molecules that consist of long chains of small repeating units) that can be made into plastics. When a container made of this plastic is thrown away, it can then be broken down by other bacteria.

As well as breaking down dangerous compounds, bacteria can also help make useful products. In 1992, scientists announced that they had found a way of turning coal into oil

◀ *Cells of the bacterium* **Escherichia coli** *show up as rodlike structures under a light microscope. Some strains of* **E. coli** *are harmless inhabitants of the human digestive system. Other strains produce toxins that make people ill.*

▲ *Blue stilton cheeses ripen at the Long Clawson Dairy in Melton Mowbray, Britain. The characteristic blue veins running through the cheese are caused by the bacterium* Penicillium glaucum. *After six weeks of maturation, the cheese is pierced from side to side with stainless steel skewers. This allows air to enter the cheese and activate the bacterial spores.*

DID YOU KNOW?

Bacteria are so small that they can only be seen through a microscope. Thousands of bacteria could fit on the period at the end of this sentence.

using bacteria. The bacteria they used are not very unusual—some of them live in the human gut. High temperatures and pressures were once needed to change coal into oil, but the new process works at around body temperature. The powdered coal is mixed with the enzymes from the bacteria and hydrogen gas in an organic fluid such as benzene (C_6H_6). The oil produced dissolves in the benzene.

A surprising discovery was made in 1992. The famous gold rushes in Alaska in the 1890s and early 1900s were triggered when people found gold nuggets in riverbeds. It seems that the nuggets may have been produced by bacteria. Scientists studied thousands of grains of gold found in the riverbeds using a scanning electron microscope to magnify them thousands of times over. The scientists found that the gold often appeared to be deposited near channels teeming with bacteria. It is possible that the bacteria concentrate the gold that is present in soil. Just how bacteria do this is still unclear. If scientists can discover the trick, however, they may be able to develop the process commercially.

Harmful bacteria

Many bacteria cause diseases in people and animals. Diphtheria, pneumonia, tuberculosis, typhoid, and whooping cough are among the many

diseases caused by these tiny living cells. Bacteria also cause various kinds of blood poisoning. Harmful bacteria are also called "germs."

Bacteria can enter the body in many ways. In many cases, people take in harmful bacteria when they consume poorly prepared food or drink contaminated water. The bacteria then produce toxins that are responsible for many cases of food poisoning. Bacteria can also enter the body through cuts in the skin. The disease tetanus results from infection by the bacterium *Clostridium tetani*. The bacteria infect open wounds and produce a toxin that blocks nerve impulses to muscles. Many sexually transmitted diseases (STDs), such as gonorrhea and syphilis, are also caused by bacteria.

Doctors now prescribe antibiotics to treat many diseases. Antibiotics prevent harmful bacteria from growing. One antibiotic is penicillin, which was discovered by Scottish bacteriologist Alexander Fleming (1881–1955). Since its discovery, penicillin has saved millions of lives. Doctors also prevent infectious diseases by vaccination—injecting weakened forms of harmful bacteria into the body. The bacteria are not strong enough to cause the disease, but they make our body prepare its defenses in case of a later infection.

▲ *Scottish bacteriologist Alexander Fleming is best known for his discovery of penicillin, which is an antibiotic produced by the fungus **Penicillium notatum**. Fleming made this important discovery by chance in 1928, when he noticed that a green mold, now known to be **Penicillium notatum**, inhibited the growth of some other bacteria.*

▶ *A bacterium called **Clostridium botulinum** produces a toxic chemical called botulinum, which may cause the killer disease called botulism.*

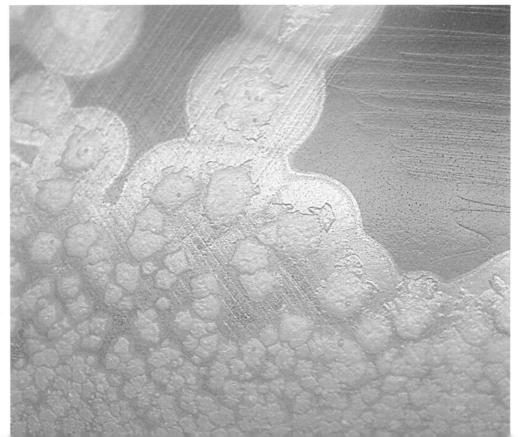

Different kinds of bacteria

Bacteria are single living cells with hard cell walls. Most are shaped like short rods and are called bacilli. Others, called spirilla, are long and curled or corkscrew shaped. Still others, called cocci, look like round balls. Sometimes bacteria change their shape, depending on where they grow.

Many of these bacteria move about by swimming or wriggling. Some have a whiplike tail, called a flagellum, and hairlike cilia that push the bacteria through the liquids in which they swim.

How bacteria multiply

Bacteria multiply by splitting in half. There are no males and females. This type of reproduction is known as asexual reproduction or binary fission. The bacterium that splits in two is called the parent cell. It produces two daughter cells that are identical to each other and to the parent cell. Most bacteria reproduce very quickly, splitting in half every 20 minutes in good conditions. If one bacterium were to divide every 20 minutes, in only six hours there would be almost half a million bacteria. The speed at which bacteria reproduce explains how bacterial diseases develop so rapidly.

In some cases, bacteria can reproduce sexually. Some bacteria are covered with hollow tubes called pili (*singular,* pilus). When sexual reproduction takes place, one bacterium fixes its pilus to another bacterium and passes genetic information through it. The bacterium that receives the genetic material is then a new individual.

flagellum

capsule

cell wall

cytoplasm

cell membrane

fimbriae

▲ *A typical bacterium has been cut away to show some of the main features. The cytoplasm is enclosed by a cell membrane and surrounded by a rigid cell wall. Some bacteria use a whiplike projection called a flagellum to move around. They may also have short projections called fimbriae to attach to surfaces.*

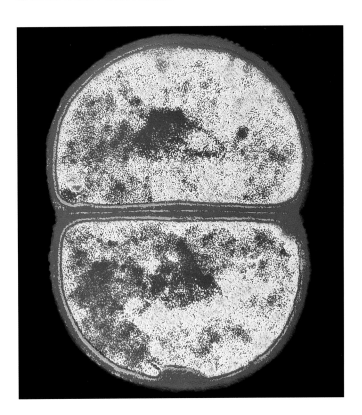

▲ *A false-color transmission electron micrograph shows a parent cell of the bacterium Staphylococcus aureus dividing into two daughter cells. The dividing cell walls are shown in red. The genetic material within the newly forming daughter cells is shown in purple.*

See also: ANTIBIOTIC • DISEASE • GENETIC ENGINEERING • VIRUS, BIOLOGICAL

Balances and weighing machines

The balance, used together with weights, was the earliest way of measuring the weight of an object. It is believed that this system has been in use for more than 4,000 years, although the oldest balances that have been found date from 2,200 years ago.

Some methods of weighing objects rely on balance—balancing the object to be weighed with other objects of a known weight or against some other form of measurable resistance. These methods can be awkward and not always very accurate. Modern weighing machines do not rely on balance. They use electronics to give fast and accurate measurements of weight.

Two-pan balances

The first balances, thought to date from about 4,000 years ago, were made of a simple beam, pivoted on a cord through its center, and with a pan hanging at each end. The article to be weighed was placed in one pan. Weights were placed in the other pan until a balance was obtained. The sum of the weights equaled the weight of the article. As these balances were hand-held and rather crude, they were not very accurate. In modern times, similar simple, hand-held balances are still used in many supermarkets throughout the world.

More modern two-pan balances work on the same principle as these early balances, but various improvements have been made to the design. One important improvement in the design of balances was made by the Romans. At the balance point, or fulcrum, of the beam, the beam rested on a triangular section. Balancing the beam on this "knife edge" made the instrument much more sensitive and accurate, especially when measuring lighter objects. This knife-edge pivot also reduced the wear of friction (rubbing force) that could make the beam uneven.

Where extreme accuracy is not necessary, a simple and strong balance can be used. For precision weighing, however, care must be taken with design and construction to improve accuracy. Chemical balances used in science laboratories are usually highly accurate two-pan designs.

Chemical balances

Chemical balances are made from specialized materials. The beams are made from a light, rigid alloy (a mixture of metals). The hard, knife-edge pivots on the beams are made from artificial sapphire. Very hard materials are chosen to reduce wear and thus maintain high accuracy. The pans of the balance hang from devices called stirrups. The stirrups are supported by hard plates resting on knife edges—one at each end of the beam.

A long pointer, fixed to the center of the beam, extends down to a scale at the bottom of the column. When the pointer is in the middle of the scale, the beam is perfectly balanced. Placing an

◀ *A shopkeeper uses electronic scales to weigh pasta for a customer. Scales are used to weigh many different kinds of consumer goods.*

object or weight on a hanging pan could damage the fine knife edges, so a mechanism is provided to lower the pans onto supports. To see if the object and weights balance, a knob can be turned to raise the beam so that the pans hang freely. A glass-sided case protects the instrument from air currents which might upset the delicate balance. The case also keeps out dirt and reduces corrosion.

Single-pan balances

Another method of weighing using a beam is to pivot the beam closer to one end than the other. This type of balance has only one pan, positioned close to the fulcrum and counterweighted by the length of the beam on the other side. A set of weights can slide along it. When unloaded, and

▼ *In this typical laboratory single-pan balance, placing an object on the pan makes the pan move down. Removing some of the small weights restores the balance. The sum of the weights removed equals the weight of the object.*

with the weights set nearest to the fulcrum, the pan and beam balance. When the pan is loaded, the weights can slide along the beam until the balance is restored. The position of the weights is checked on a scale on the beam, giving the weight of the object in the pan. This type of scaled balance was developed by the Romans, who called it a steelyard.

While two-pan balances rely on having exactly the right combination of weights to balance the load being weighed, the scale on a single-pan balance is much quicker to use and can be even more accurate. The single-pan balance is widely used in industrial, medical, and science laboratories throughout the world. The single-pan balance has become more popular than the two-pan balance because it is so easy to use. A larger version of this type of weighing machine was once used to weigh large objects such as carts of coal. A disadvantage of this was that the heavy cart had to be suspended from the beam.

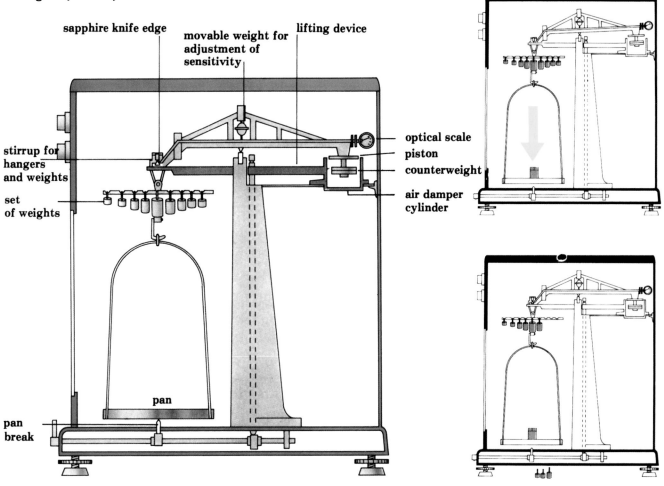

sapphire knife edge

movable weight for adjustment of sensitivity

lifting device

stirrup for hangers and weights

set of weights

optical scale

piston

counterweight

air damper cylinder

pan

pan break

Damping

In single and two-pan balances, the pointer swings from side to side for a while before coming to rest. In sensitive balances, this could take a long time. So a technique called damping is used to bring the beam and pointer to rest quickly.

The most common system is called pneumatic damping. One end of the beam moves a loose-fitting piston in a cylinder. When it moves, the piston forces air in or out of the cylinder. As one end of the cylinder is sealed, the piston has to force the air through the small gap between the piston and cylinder. This effort prevents the piston from moving quickly, so the beam comes gently to rest with little vibration.

Pendulum balance

With a pendulum balance, a weighing plate is balanced against a fixed weight or pendulum through a series of levers pivoted on knife edges. The pendulum is pulled by gravity to hang vertically. When an object is placed on the weighing plate, it pulls the pendulum up until the pendulum and weighing plate balance. A pointer attached to the pendulum moves around an arc-shaped scale and indicates the weight of the object.

Spring balance

Another type of weighing machine balances the weight of an object attached to one end of a spring against the extension (stretching) of the spring. The extension of the spring is a measure of the weight of the object being weighed. This type of machine was developed in the seventeenth century and was the first self-indicating weighing machine. Early spring balances were not very accurate, because the springs used were not very stretchy and they suffered from expansion and contraction with changing temperatures. Modern spring balances are now as accurate as pendulum balances.

ELECTRONIC WEIGHING MACHINES

Since the development of transistor circuits and then large-scale integrated circuits, mechanical weighing machines have largely been replaced by

▲ *In this example, a single-pan balance has the pan positioned above the beam rather than hanging below it. The counterweight can slide along the long arm until the arm is level. The weight is then read from the scale.*

extremely accurate electronic machines. One of the earliest electronic weighing machines was partly mechanical, however. It used a weighing plate and a spring. Instead of a pointer moving over a scale, the movement of the spring caused a coded disk to rotate. A light shone on the disk and, depending on the pattern on the disk, various light-sensitive electronic detectors were activated. Different weights were indicated by different patterns on the disk. The different light-sensitive detectors gave an appropriate reading of the weight.

Strain-gauge transducers

Modern weighing machines usually use strain-gauge transducers. These are electronic devices in which the strain on the weighing plate, which is proportional to the load, is measured by electrical resistance. The output of the strain-gauge transducer is a voltage that is in proportion to the load. Integrated circuits use this proportional voltage to activate a digital display of the weight. A built-in calculator can also make use of the price per pound or kilogram to give a digital display of the cost of the weighed item. This type of electronic scale is typical of the weighing machines used in most supermarkets.

Weighing stations

In the seventeenth century, English inventor John Wyatt (1700–1766) developed the weigh bridge or weighing station to weigh large objects such as carts. The cart was pulled onto a weigh plate, and a system of levers transferred the weight to a beam, pivoted close to one end. The load was balanced by proportional weights attached to the long arm of the beam. This type of weighing station was not very accurate, but performance was improved when the proportional weights were replaced with a steelyard system of sliding weights and a scale.

A self-indicating weighing station was then developed, in which a counterweight was suspended in a tank of water. When a vehicle, such as a cart, was wheeled onto the weighing platform, a lever connected to the counterweight lifted the counterweight slowly up out of the water. As it left the water, the counterweight lost its buoyancy (tendency to float in water) and eventually balanced the load. A chain connected to the lever passed around a drum and caused a pointer on the drum to move, indicating the weight.

In the early twentieth century, the pendulum balance system was added to the industrial weighing station. Instead of a fixed pointer moving

▲ *Electronic bathroom scales are an example of an electronic weighing machine. Such machines can be used for many applications where balances cannot.*

through an arc, however, a rack-and-pinion gear system gave 360 degrees of rotation to the pointer. Weights could also be added to the pendulum, giving an accurate weight indicator that could be used over a wide range of weights.

Electronic weighing stations

The principle of electric weighing stations is the same as that of small electronic weighing machines. A vehicle, such as a truck, is driven onto the weighing station, and strain-gauge transducers give a reading of the weight of the vehicle. The advantage of using electronics is that the weight indicator does not have to be in the same place as the weighing station—it could be in an office a distance away. The electronic output from the weighing station can also be linked to a computer so that the information can be recorded.

Modern electronic weighing stations on railroads are sensitive enough to allow individual freight cars to be weighed while they are coupled and moving. In the short time that a freight car is on the weighing station, many weight measurements are taken. When all the measurements are averaged, an accurate reading of the weight can be displayed.

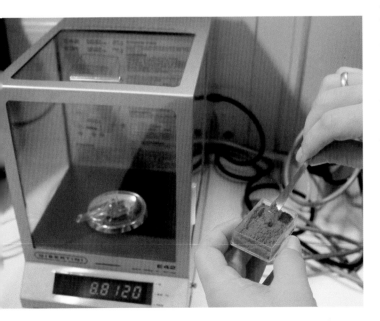

▲ *A scientist uses a set of electronic scales to weigh a set amount of a chemical substance. Accurate weighing is vital in chemistry and other scientific disciplines.*

See also: MASS AND WEIGHT

Ballistics

Ballistics is a branch of science that deals with the movement of projectiles such as bullets and rockets. The three main branches of this science deal with the firing, flight, and final damage of the projectile.

The study of ballistics is important in areas such as the manufacture of ammunition and in forensic science. Ballistics is divided into interior, exterior, and terminal ballistics.

Interior ballistics

Interior ballistics deals with the firing of projectiles. A gun, for example, fires bullets. A device called a firing pin strikes the bullet's casing, setting off an explosive powder contained inside. This produces gases that expand rapidly, forcing the bullet out of the gun barrel. Specialists in internal ballistics design guns and ammunition according to the range and effect required.

Unlike a bullet, a rocket carries the fuel that propels it. The fuel continues burning after the rocket has been launched.

Exterior ballistics

Exterior ballistics is the study of a projectile's flight path. For a bullet, the path (trajectory) resembles a curve called a parabola. Various forces affect the movement of the bullet. Earth's gravity makes it

▼ *A round of ammunition is loaded into the chamber of a revolver. The main brass part of the round contains the propellant, which fires the bullet (the lead tip) out of the gun barrel.*

curve gradually toward the ground. If there is no obstacle in its path, the bullet will travel farthest when fired at an angle of 45 degrees to the ground.

Air tends to resist the motion of the bullet and also tilt its nose upward. As a result, the bullet slows down and tends to tumble through the air. To prevent this tumbling motion, and keep it pointing forward, the bullet twists out of the gun barrel. This is done by means of a spiral groove in the barrel, called rifling. Like a gyroscope, the spinning bullet resists being tilted. In arrows and rockets, the problem is overcome by fitting tail fins, which increase the air resistance at the back of the projectile so that the nose always stays in front.

The path of a rocket is controlled by the thrust of its engines. When the engines are switched off, the rocket may fall to the ground. However, if the rocket has gone high enough through the

atmosphere before the engines are switched off, it may go into orbit around Earth or even escape from it altogether and head into outer space.

Terminal ballistics

Terminal ballistics is the study of the damage done by missiles to their targets. The damage may be caused in various ways.

Shells destroy their targets by explosion or fire. Bullets damage tissues by impact and penetration. High-speed bullets can pass right through the body, causing damage between the entry and exit points.

High-speed bullets are unsuitable for police fighting street crimes, because the bullet could pass through the criminal and hit an innocent person. Instead, low-speed bullets that spread out on impact are used. These bullets are designed to lodge in the target.

▼ *A ballistics researcher fires rounds of ammunition from an automatic weapon in a test range. Ammunition is specifically designed for different weapons and uses.*

See also: EXPLOSIVE • GUN • ROCKET

Balloon

Balloons are the one form of lighter-than-air craft that span the entire history of piloted flight. They were the means by which people first took to the air in the eighteenth century. Today, balloons have many uses, from recreation to scientific research.

Heavier-than-air machines, such as airplanes and gliders, create a lifting force by moving through the air. This force holds them up. By contrast, a balloon is a lighter-than-air device. It moves with the air and obtains its lifting force by means of displacement. This means that it displaces a volume of air and puts something lighter in its place, for example, hydrogen gas or hot air. Since the balloon and its contents are lighter than the displaced air, the balloon floats.

Imagine what happens when a volume of still air in the atmosphere is displaced by the same volume of a lighter gas. If a volume of air is still, it must be because the air pressure below holds it up. When the volume of air is displaced by a lighter gas, the air pressure below remains the same, but now it has a lighter gas to support, so the air pressure is sufficient to force the lighter gas upward. If the gas is contained in a balloon, the whole structure will be pushed up higher in the air column. This happens if the balloon and its load are not too heavy to be lifted as well.

A balloon is said to be in equilibrium in the air column when it remains balanced at the same height. The total weight of the balloon and its contents is then the same as the weight of the air that it displaces. The pressure that would have supported the air is, therefore, just enough to support the balloon instead. For this reason, the balloon stays at the same height.

The lifting force of a balloon depends on the gas that fills it. At sea level, 1,000 cubic feet (28 cubic meters) of hot air at 212°F (100°C) can lift a load of 17 pounds (8 kilograms) when the surrounding air is at 60°F (16°C). A similar volume of hydrogen would lift a load of 70 pounds (32 kilograms). Helium, another gas used to fill balloons, would lift a load of 65 pounds (30 kilograms).

For the greatest amount of lift, hydrogen is obviously the best gas to use in balloons. But cost, convenience, and safety are also important. Today, hydrogen, helium, and hot-air balloons all have their different uses.

History of ballooning

The first aircraft that took to the skies under its own power was a balloon designed by French paper manufacturer Joseph Montgolfier (1740–1810), who was assisted by his younger brother Jacques Étienne. In June 1783, in Annonay, France, they gave a public demonstration of a flight that lasted for ten minutes and covered more than 1 mile (1.6 kilometers). The craft had no one in it and made what is called a captive flight. A long rope was attached to the balloon so that it could be held from below and only rise so far. The balloon was filled with hot air provided by a large fire on the ground.

The Montgolfier brothers' balloon created great interest. Soon other people began to investigate ballooning.

▶ *Hot-air ballooning is a popular pastime for many people, although it is expensive. Balloons can be made in many shapes, colors, and sizes. Ballooning events draw large crowds who come to watch the colorful spectacle.*

French physicist Jaques Charles (1746–1823) thought that the Montgolfier brothers must have used hydrogen, so he designed a balloon filled with hydrogen. Hydrogen is lighter than air, so it tends to rise even at normal temperatures and needs no heating. On August 27, 1783, Charles released his balloon from a field in Paris. It landed 15 miles (24 kilometers) away, near the village of Gonesse.

Five months after demonstrating the first unpiloted balloon flight, the Montgolfier brothers were ready to put the first people up in a balloon. The pilots on this historic voyage were Jean-François Pilâtre de Rozier and Major François d'Arlandes. The two tried several captive flights

▲ *In Bois de Boulogne, France, in 1783, Jean-François Pilâtre de Rozier and Major François d'Arlandes were the first people to fly in a hot-air balloon. The balloon was designed by the French Montgolfier brothers.*

before ascending in a free flight on November 21, 1783. The balloon, launched in Paris, crossed the Seine River at a height of 1,000 feet (300 meters). It landed 25 minutes later, a little more than 5 miles (8 kilometers) away. Their balloon was a flimsy craft made from cloth backed with paper. It measured 75 feet (23 meters) high by nearly 50 feet (15 meters) across. An onboard furnace burning chopped straw heated the air. The balloon nearly caught fire, but the pilots managed to land safely.

The first piloted hydrogen balloon flight was made on December 1, 1783, by Jacques Charles and M. N. Robert. Their balloon, made of silk coated with rubber to make it airtight, took them from Paris to Nesles, about 27 miles (43 kilometers) away. Because of the risk of the early hot-air balloons catching fire, the hydrogen balloon was soon regarded as superior.

Balloons at war

In the American Civil War (1861–1865), both armies used balloons as military lookout posts. These balloons were tied to the ground by means of long cables. From their position high above the ground, the observers could see enemy troops many miles away.

Balloons were also used for observation in World War I (1914–1918), although this job was gradually taken over by the early powered airplanes. The advantage of the airplane was that it could be steered. The balloon, if released, could only go where the wind took it.

From the 1850s, long, propeller-driven balloons called airships were developed. As these airships did not need to rely on wind direction, they proved of great use to the armed forces. Germany and Britain used airships during World War I for both observation and bombing raids.

Modern hot-air balloons

Due to improved design and the use of flame-retardant materials, modern hot-air balloons are safer than gas balloons. They are also cheaper and easier to operate. The tapering bottom of the balloon, called the envelope, is usually made from nylon material. Nylon tapes sewn to the envelope support the basket and a gas burner that heats the air. Modern burners use propane gas, blowing the hot air up into the bottom of the envelope. The balloon is made to rise by turning on the burner to heat the air. Turning off the burner allows the air to cool again, so that the balloon goes down.

Modern gas balloons

Gas balloons are filled with hydrogen or helium. Hot-air balloons are not called gas balloons, even though air is a mixture of gases. Most gas balloons are filled with hydrogen. Great care must be taken with hydrogen, because it is highly flammable and forms an explosive mixture when combined with air. Helium is safe as it does not burn, and it produces almost as much lift as hydrogen. However, helium is more expensive than hydrogen in most countries, except in the United States.

Modern gas balloons for piloted flight have a round envelope made from fabric sealed with rubber or neoprene. Around the envelope is a thin rope net with a horizontal ring hanging from it. A basket carrying the crew and equipment is hung from this ring.

As a balloon rises, the surrounding air pressure gradually decreases. As a result, the gas in the balloon is able to expand. To prevent the balloon from bursting, a gas escape tube is provided at the bottom of the envelope. This tube, called the appendix, acts as a valve. It allows some gas to escape, but prevents the entry of air into the envelope. A gas balloon is made to rise by throwing sand bags or other heavy objects from the basket. To come down, gas is released through a small valve in the top of the envelope. The valve is operated by a cord leading down into the basket.

Ballooning as a sport

The early balloons provided daring sport for their brave pilots. Once reliable balloons had been developed, numerous contests and races were organized. Today, ballooning events are held all over world. Big crowds go to see the impressive sight of the large, colorful balloons filling the sky.

▲ *U.S. pilot Steve Fossett stands on the capsule of his* **Bud Lite Spirit of Freedom** *balloon after landing in the Australian outback in July 2002. He completed the first solo circumnavigation of the world by balloon.*

Scientific balloons

Unpiloted gas-filled balloons are often used for weather observation and scientific research. Weather balloons carry instruments that measure temperature, pressure, humidity, and other atmospheric conditions. The measurements can be sent back to the ground automatically by radio, or they can be recorded on charts by an instrument carried in the balloon. In the latter case, scientists have to recover the instrument pack when the balloon returns to the ground to obtain the information they require.

See also: AIR • HYDROGEN • WEATHER SYSTEM

Bar code and scanner

A bar code is a series of printed stripes that carries information, such as the name, category, and price of a grocery item. A scanner uses light beams to read the information in a way that a computer can understand.

Look on almost any grocery or product label, and it will have a bar code somewhere on the packaging. A bar code is a group of side-by-side black stripes of different thicknesses, with a string of numbers underneath. When a shopper takes an item to the checkout, the cashier passes the bar code under a scanner to record details of the sale on the cash register. The register then displays the price of the item, often with its name, and adds it to the shopper's total bill. The cash register records the information from each transaction each day, so the store manager knows what has been sold.

What is the code?

The code in a bar code is the same as the string of numbers underneath, but in a form easy for a scanner to read. The system used for shop-bought goods in the United States is the Universal Product Code (UPC), and it is administered by the Uniform Code Council (UCC).

A standard UPC number has 12 digits. The UCC decides the first six digits—these identify the type of product and the manufacturer. The manufacturer adds the next five digits to identify the exact product. Storekeepers use this information to program their cash registers and assign prices. Some UPCs use only eight digits, but they can take in extra zeros to make a standard 12-digit code.

DID YOU KNOW?

The Association of American Railroads used simple bar codes as early as 1967, seven years before store chains. Railroad workers would use brush widths to handpaint two stripes on freight cars. Trackside scanners in switching yards read the passing codes to check where each car of an incoming train was headed.

The last digit in a bar code is the check digit. It helps to prevent scanning errors. When the scanner reads the main part of the bar code, it does a routine calculation using all the digits. The result should match the check digit. If not, something has gone wrong during the scan, and the bar code fails to register. When this happens, the cashier has to key the number code into the register by hand.

Scanning the code

While a person reads the number code on a label, scanners read the stripes. Handheld scanners use rotating mirrors to run a laser beam over the bar code. Other scanners shine laser beams up through a glass plate in front of the cashier.

◀ A sales clerk uses a bar code scanner at a store's checkout. Bar codes contain price information and identify each individual product for the cash register.

▶ *A picture of a bar code, showing what the different numbers and bars represent.*

▼ *A parking attendant uses a handheld scanner to read the bar code on a vehicle parking ticket. This helps him check if the car has been parked for too long.*

Twin bars mark the start, middle, and end.

0   1234 5 67890   5

manufacturer   product   check

0	Standard UPC (8 digit or 12 digit)
6 or 7	Standard UPC (12 digit only)
2	Weighed goods (such as fruits and vegetables)
3	Drugs and personal-care products (such as soaps and shampoos)
4	Store's own bar code (not part of the UPC system)
5	Coupons and vouchers

When the laser beam passes over a white stripe in the bar code, it reflects back onto a light sensor in the scanner. Black stripes hardly reflect the laser beam at all. The sensor produces a small current when the laser reflects back on it, so the current from the sensor mimics the varying brightness of the bar code from one side to the other.

Each bar code starts and ends with a pair of thin lines. From these lines, a processor in the scanner recognizes when to start and finish reading the bar code. A third pair of thin lines marks the center of the bar code. Stripe patterns for each number differ from one side of this mark to the other.

Other types and uses

The World Product Code (WPC) brings together the UPC and similar systems from countries across the world. It does this by using a 13-digit code—a zero before a standard U.S. bar code converts it into a World Product Code. In other countries, the WPC starts with a two-digit country code and has a shorter manufacturer code.

Some bar code systems use stripe patterns to encode letters and symbols as well as numbers. An example is the military Code 39, which can encode up to 128 characters, while UPCs only encode numbers. Code 39 bar codes can be any length, so they can carry much more information than a 13-digit WPC or 12-digit UPC bar code.

Bar codes also appear on drivers' licences, name tags, and bankers' checks. In all cases, they are there to make the document readable by machines. Many countries' postal services now encourage the use of bar codes to represent ZIP codes, because bar codes make it easier to sort the mail by machine.

See also: COMPUTER • LASER

Barometer

Air pressure is caused by the weight of the air pressing down on Earth's surface. Barometers are used to predict changes in the weather by measuring changes in air pressure. Generally, low air pressure is a sign of bad weather, and increasing air pressure is a sign that good weather is on the way.

Italian scientist Galileo Galilei (1564–1642) was the first person to show that the atmosphere has weight and exerts pressure on Earth's surface. It was Galileo's pupil, Evangelista Torricelli (1608–1647), who invented the mercury barometer in 1643.

Torricelli took a long glass tube with one open end and one closed end and filled it with the liquid metal mercury, taking care that no air bubbles got into the tube. He then placed the open end in a dish filled with more mercury. The column of mercury in the tube dropped until it was 30 inches (76 centimeters) above the level in the dish. The space above the mercury column, now known as the Torricellian vacuum, contained nothing but a little mercury vapor at low pressure.

In Torricelli's barometer, the air pressure on the mercury in the dish held up the mercury column in the glass tube. The height of the column changed as the air pressure changed, so measuring the height of the mercury column gave an indication of the air pressure. However, measuring the height of the mercury column was not so simple.

One way to measure the height of the mercury column is to use a ruler fixed to the tube. The zero mark on the ruler should be lined up with the level of the mercury in the dish. The height can then be measured simply by noting the reading on the ruler opposite the top of the mercury column.

However, an increase in air pressure will push the level in the dish down, so that the level in the tube rises. And a decrease in air pressure will allow the level in the dish to rise, so that the level in the tube falls. So, as the level in the tube changes, the zero mark must move to line up with the level in the dish. Only then will the reading on the ruler be a true measure of the height.

Having to reset the scale before taking a reading was not very convenient. But this problem was overcome in later versions of the mercury barometer—the Fortin and Kew designs.

The Fortin barometer

French inventor Jean Fortin (1750–1831) invented the barometer that bears his name in 1800. Fortin fixed a scale to the glass tube and adjusted the lower mercury level to a zero mark before taking a reading. The mercury container, or cistern, at the bottom consisted of a flexible leather bag, which rested on an adjusting screw. Turning the screw raised or lowered the mercury level until it touched an ivory pointer fixed in position above the surface of the mercury. A clear reflection of the ivory pointer could be seen in the silvery surface of the mercury. So any gap between the pointer and the

▲ *Italian scientist Evangelista Torricelli is best known for his invention of the mercury barometer.*

▲ *Aneroid barometers are cheap to produce, so they are popular for use at home. Aneroid barometers are not as accurate as mercury barometers, but they give a rough prediction of the impending weather.*

mercury was seen as a gap double the size between the pointer and its reflection. If the pointer was slightly submerged, its tip could not be seen. This arrangement allowed an accurate setting of the mercury level. After setting the lower mercury level, the height of the mercury column could be measured on the fixed scale.

The Kew barometer

The Kew barometer is a mercury barometer that needs no zero adjustment. Unlike the Fortin barometer, the cistern of the Kew barometer is rigid, usually made from iron or steel, and has parallel sides. As a result, the mercury level in the cistern always changes by the same amount for each inch that the mercury column rises or falls.

Imagine that a change in air pressure causes the column of mercury to rise by one inch. As the mercury rises up the column, the level of mercury in the cistern will drop. So the height of the column, measured to the surface in the cistern, will have increased by just over 1 inch (2.5 centimeters). For the mercury column to rise by exactly one inch, it would actually move a little less than this distance to compensate for the drop in the level of mercury in the cistern. As a result, the fixed scale used to calculate the height of the mercury column has to

be compressed. The distance between each inch mark on the scale is slightly less than a true inch, the difference rarely being more than 5 percent.

Kew barometers are designed to be portable. They must be tilted carefully so that the mercury fills the glass tube. Then they can be carried upside down without the risk of spilling the mercury. It is important to stop the air from reaching the top of the tube, because it would push the mercury down slightly and cause inaccurate readings. Therefore, the tube has an air trap to catch rising bubbles.

DID YOU KNOW?

The main advantage of using mercury in a barometer is that it is very dense. A given volume of mercury weighs 13.6 times as much as the same volume of water. If water was used to balance the pressure of the atmosphere, the column would be 13.6 times as long as a column of mercury—34 feet (10 meters) instead of 30 inches (76 centimeters).

Aneroid barometer

French scientist Lucien Vidie (1805–1866) invented the aneroid barometer in 1843. Aneroid barometers contain a vacuum inside a sealed metal chamber called the vacuum capsule or bellows. The vacuum capsule is disk shaped with flexible corrugated (grooved) sides, which are held apart by a steel spring. The separation between the corrugated sides depends on the pressure of the air.

As the air pressure changes, the corrugated sides move in or out. This movement is very small, but it is magnified by a system of levers. The final lever moves a wire or fine chain wound around a spindle, making it turn against the force of a weak coiled spring. A pointer on the end of the spindle indicates the air pressure on a circular scale.

See also: AIR • MERCURY, METAL • METEOROLOGY

Battery

Batteries produce electricity by means of a chemical reaction. They are used wherever a portable supply of electrical power is needed. Pocket calculators, flashlights, and automatic cameras all work using batteries.

An electric cell is a device that generates electricity by means of a chemical reaction. A cell produces an electrical force called a voltage. Batteries consist of a number of connected cells that increase the voltage that is produced.

Experiments with electricity were carried out long before cells and batteries were invented. Some scientists experimented with electricity generated by friction (rubbing) machines. Others gathered the electricity released during thunderstorms.

Galvani's frogs

The work that led to the discovery and use of electric current started with a scientific argument between two Italian professors. They were Luigi Galvani (1737–1798), who was a physician and professor of anatomy at Bologna University, and Alessandro Volta (1745–1827), who was a professor of physics at Pavia University.

In 1771, Luigi Galvani prepared an experiment using some dead frogs. A thunderstorm was approaching, and Galvani wanted to see what effect the electricity in the air would have on the frogs. While Galvani was setting up the experiment, he found that the frogs' legs, which were on copper

▶ *Batteries await safe disposal at a recycling center. Disposing of batteries can pose serious environmental problems because they contain very corrosive chemicals.*

hooks, twitched whenever they were hung on an iron railing. Galvani realized that electricity caused the frogs' legs to move. He had, accidentally, produced a small, but fairly steady, supply of electricity. In other words, Galvani had made a simple form of electric cell.

Galvani realized that electricity caused the contractions (drawing together) of the muscles in the frogs' legs, but he did not know where it came from. Galvani decided that the electricity was in the bodies of all animals, and the nerves were the conductors (carriers) for it.

Volta's pile

Alessandro Volta thought that Galvani was wrong. Volta had already invented several instruments to collect electrical charges and measure electricity. He was certain that the twitch in the frogs' legs was caused by an electric current produced between the

▲ *In 1800, Italian physicist Alessandro Volta invented the first battery, called the voltaic pile. This important invention prompted the start of a scientific and technological revolution.*

two different metals. A lively public debate followed, and Volta devoted himself to proving that his idea was correct.

Volta believed that if a dry conductor (such as a piece of metal) was placed between two wet conductors, or if two dry conductors were placed together with one wet conductor, and the conductors were connected to form a circuit, this arrangement would set up a circulation of electricity. Moreover, Volta said that this circulation would not stop until the circuit was broken.

Volta piled up the dry and wet conductors in sets of three. He used a silver coin, a zinc plate, and a piece of wet cardboard. When he touched the two ends of the pile, he felt a shock. This arrangement had created an electric current, just as he had thought. Volta kept adding sets of three conductors and found that the higher the pile, the stronger the electric current. Soon Volta had built a tower of conductors up to 60 sets high, which he kept in position with rods. Sparks appeared when wire leads were attached at each end, and the flow of electricity was continuous.

Volta announced his discovery to the Royal Society in London, Britain, in March 1800. The invention was called the voltaic pile. This was a very important discovery, because it provided scientists with a steady flow of electricity to use for their research. The battery was a store of electricity, which could be drawn off as needed. Capacitors had been used to store electricity produced by friction, but they discharge quickly, with the current falling to zero. Batteries, therefore, made it much easier for scientists to work with electricity.

How cells work

Since Volta's time, many types of electric cells have been invented. The basic principle of operation is the same in each case. An electric current (a flow of tiny charged particles called electrons) is made to flow between two plates called electrodes. A chemical solution called the electrolyte separates the electrodes. When the two plates are connected by a wire, an electric circuit is generated. An electric circuit is a completed path around which electricity passes.

Completion of the electric circuit causes chemical reactions to take place at the electrodes of the cell. At one electrode, the reactions cause free electrons to be produced. These electrons flow out around the circuit and back to the other electrode. Electrons have a negative electric charge, so the electrode from which they flow is called the negative electrode. The other electrode is called the positive electrode.

When a cell is in use, the chemical reactions that take place gradually change the electrolyte. Eventually, the cell runs out of power and can no longer supply any current.

Primary and secondary cells

Most cells have to be replaced when they have run down. Cells of this type are called primary cells. The batteries commonly used in flashlights, portable stereos, and electrical toys are primary cells. Other cells can be used again after recharging with electricity. These are called secondary cells, accumulators, or storage cells.

DID YOU KNOW?

In 1999, British electricity generator National Power announced plans to build the world's biggest battery in Britain. The planned $22 million rechargable system will store 20 megawatt-hours of energy, with a peak output of 14 megawatts, in a building the size of a two-story house.

Storage cells are recharged by connecting them to a charger. This is powered by a domestic electricity supply and produces a suitable source for recharging the cells. Recharging takes several hours and reverses the chemical reactions that took place when the cells were in use. As a result, the electrolyte is gradually restored. When the process is finished, the cells are ready for use again.

A typical automobile battery has six connected storage cells. An electricity generator, turned by the automobile engine, normally keeps the battery well charged. But the battery can run down if the engine is not running and the lights are left on for a long period. Then the battery will have to be connected to a charger to restore it to full working order.

A simple cell

The Daniell cell is a simple cell that was used in the early telegraph stations. It consists of a zinc electrode suspended in a solution of zinc sulfate ($ZnSO_4$), and a copper electrode suspended in a solution of copper sulfate ($CuSO_4$). The two solutions are separated by a porous barrier that allows ions to pass through but prevents the solutions from mixing together.

At the zinc electrode, the zinc atoms dissolve in the zinc sulfate solution. Each zinc atom leaves an electron behind so that the electrode has a negative charge. At the copper electrode, copper ions from the copper sulfate solution are deposited on the electrode, giving it a positive charge. When the electrodes are connected by a wire, electrons flow from the zinc electrode to the copper electrode, creating an electric current. As the electrons pass

from the zinc electrode to the copper electrode, more zinc dissolves into the zinc sulfate solution and more copper ions are deposited on the copper electrode. And so the process continues. The overall cell reaction can be written like this:

$$Zn + CuSO_4 \rightarrow Cu + ZnSO_4$$
zinc + copper sulfate → copper + zinc sulfate

If the porous barrier were removed, the zinc electrode would react directly with the copper sulfate and would become coated with copper, bringing the reaction to a stop.

Problems with cells

Unless precautions are taken, cells suffer from side effects that limit their action or shorten their life. In the Daniell cell, the zinc that makes up the negative electrode must be extremely pure. Most zinc

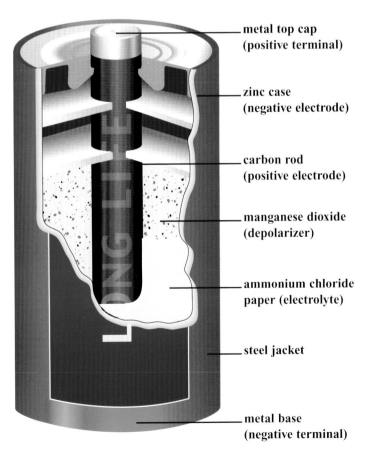

metal top cap (positive terminal)

zinc case (negative electrode)

carbon rod (positive electrode)

manganese dioxide (depolarizer)

ammonium chloride paper (electrolyte)

steel jacket

metal base (negative terminal)

▲ *A diagram of a dry cell battery showing the different components. Dry cell batteries are the most common form of primary cells.*

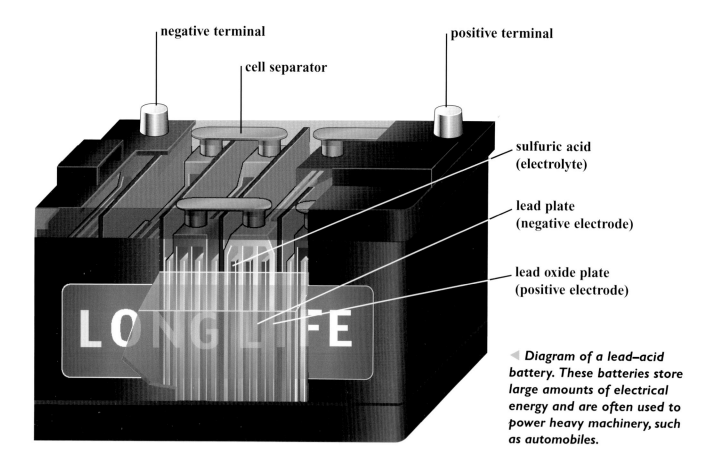

negative terminal

cell separator

positive terminal

sulfuric acid
(electrolyte)

lead plate
(negative electrode)

lead oxide plate
(positive electrode)

◀ *Diagram of a lead–acid battery. These batteries store large amounts of electrical energy and are often used to power heavy machinery, such as automobiles.*

contains iron as an impurity. In the acid, this would react with the zinc plate and cause it to be eaten away. This effect is called local action.

Another problem is called polarization. This effect is usually caused by a gas forming at one of the electrodes. In the Daniell cell, hydrogen bubbles form at the copper electrode. After a while, a layer of bubbles covers the electrode and prevents the cell from working properly. Modern cells are carefully designed to minimize local action and polarization.

Modern cells and batteries

Dry cells contain no free liquid. A zinc case acts as the negative electrode. The electrolyte is ammonium chloride (NH_4Cl) dissolved in water and soaked in a layer of absorbent paper. A central carbon rod acts as the positive electrode. The cell is filled with a chemical paste, such as manganese dioxide (MnO_2), that reduces polarization.

Dry cell batteries are by far the most common type of battery, and they power many household electrical goods. However, many of these goods may use more modern and sophisticated batteries. Many modern batteries are designed to be rechargable. Although they cost more than standard dry cell batteries, they can be recharged time and time again and are much cheaper in the long run. Some common rechargable batteries include nickel-cadmium, nickel-metal hydride, and lithium-ion cells.

Lead-acid batteries are used in modern automobiles (see the illustration above). They have six two-volt (2V) cells connected in a series to give the battery a twelve-volt (12V) standard output. These batteries are also rechargable.

Many other types of cells and batteries are also used to power many different devices. These range from tiny mercury cells used in hearing aids to huge fuel cells constantly supplied with chemical fuel so they never run down.

See also: CAPACITOR • CHEMICAL REACTION • ELECTRICITY • FUEL CELL

Bearing

The ancient Egyptians used bearings to move the huge stones needed to build the pyramids. Logs were placed under the stones so that they could be rolled along easily. Many modern bearings work on a similar principle.

Friction is the name given to forces that tend to prevent movement. To slide one object over another, a force must be used to overcome the friction between the two objects. The friction between rough surfaces is far greater than the friction between smooth surfaces.

When force is used to overcome friction, some of the energy used up changes into heat. When striking a match, for example, the friction between the match and the box produces enough heat to light the chemicals in the match head. In machines, friction wastes energy and causes moving parts to wear out. Bearings reduce friction and so improve the performance of many machines.

Bearings can be designed to support moving parts that rotate or slide. Most bearings are used to support rotating parts. The three main types are rolling-element, fluid-film, and rubbing bearings.

▲ *A worker carefully removes a container of hot bearing rings from an oven. Bearings often must be able to withstand very high loads. Heat treatment makes them as tough as possible.*

ROLLING-ELEMENT BEARINGS

Rolling-element bearings use precision-made rollers or balls between a fixed and a moving surface. The most common type of rolling-element bearing consists of four main parts: an inner ring called a race; a set of rollers or balls; a device called a cage to keep the rolling elements in position; and an outer race. The cage is made of soft steel, brass, or plastic resin, because it does not need to be strong. All the other parts are made of hard steel so that they can bear heavy loads.

In machines where a load presses at right angles to the turning shaft in the inner race, ball bearings are normally used. Bearings with rollers can be used to withstand thrust along the shaft. Automobile wheels are often mounted on tapered roller bearings. These are designed to support the weight of the vehicle. They also withstand sideways forces produced when the vehicle is cornering.

Lubrication

For long life and quiet operation, rolling-element bearings must be lubricated with oil or grease. This allows the moving parts to slide over each other easily. Most of these bearings are packed with grease. In heavy industrial machines, where a lot of heat is produced in the bearings, circulating oil is

◄ *Rolling-element bearings called ball-journal bearings are used where there is a fixed load at right angles to the inner bearing race, such as on a driveshaft.*

used as the lubricant. Besides ensuring that the operation of the bearings is smooth, the oil flow also removes the heat generated by friction. The warmed oil coming from the bearings is cooled before being passed through the system again. Special greases have been developed for the bearings on vehicles designed to stay in space for long periods. Ordinary greases tend to dry up in the vacuum of outer space.

FLUID-FILM BEARINGS

In fluid-film bearings, friction between the rubbing surfaces is reduced by a film of fluid instead of balls or rollers. The fluid is usually oil, but it can be water or even a gas such as air. It can be convenient to use water-film bearings in a water pump.

The two main kinds of fluid-film bearings are the hydrodynamic and hydrostatic types. In both these types of bearings, the fluid film must force the moving surface away from the fixed one. In the hydrodynamic bearing, the fluid is drawn in by the rotation of the moving part. In the hydrostatic bearing, the fluid is supplied under pressure from an external source.

Hydrodynamic bearings

Most fluid-film bearings are hydrodynamic. They are used in machines where the speed of rotation is sufficient to draw in the fluid between the surfaces. Automobile engine crankshaft bearings, for example, operate on this principle. Although a pump supplies oil to the bearings, the pressure is not sufficient to separate the surfaces.

In all hydrodynamic bearings, the surfaces touch each other when starting or stopping, because there is not enough rotation speed to draw in the oil. So the bearings have to be made from materials that will allow a certain amount of friction.

Similar bearings using air as a lubricant instead of liquid are called aerodynamic bearings. These are suitable for high-speed machines with light loads, for example, textile spinning equipment.

Hydrostatic bearings

Hydrostatic bearings need a pumped supply of fluid at a pressure high enough to separate the surfaces. Such bearings are used to support heavy loads moving at low speeds. Most hydrostatic bearings resemble hydrodynamic bearings, but they have some provision for pumping in the fluid.

Aerostatic bearings work on the same principle but use an air film and work at high speed. Dental drills use this type of bearing.

RUBBING BEARINGS

Rubbing bearings made from plastic materials can operate without lubrication. The two surfaces make direct contact. Self-lubricating rubbing bearings are made from spongy metal containing oil. Rubbing bearings are cheap to produce, but they are suitable only for light loads.

► *Roller bearings are rolling-element bearings that can support heavy loads and are found in many different types of machinery.*

See also: FRICTION

Bicycle

Cycling is a very popular way of getting around. Many people like to ride to school or to work. Some cyclists are professional sports people. Still others cycle just for fun. Bicycle design has come a long way since the first wooden machines appeared early in the eighteenth century. High-tech materials such as carbon fiber and titanium alloys are now used to produce many different bicycles.

Scottish blacksmith Kirkpatrick Macmillan (1812–1878) built the first pedal-operated bicycle in 1839. Before then, bicycles such as the "Hobby Horse," built by German Baron Karl Drais von Sauerbronn (1785–1851), did not have pedals. The Hobby Horse moved forward when the cyclist placed his or her feet on the ground and walked forward. Macmillan's machine worked by pedaling levers with each foot. Connecting rods transferred the movement of the levers to metal arms called cranks. The cranks converted the up-and-down movement of the levers into the turning movement of the rear wheel.

By the late 1860s, many developments in bicycle design made cycling more popular in Europe and the United States. Strong, wire-spoked wheels appeared in 1870. Nine years later, chain-driven bicycles were developed. Pedal-driven cranks connected to the front wheel of these bikes by a chain and toothed wheels called sprockets.

The invention of pneumatic (air-filled) rubber tires by British veterinary surgeon John Boyd Dunlop (1840–1921) in 1888 made cycling more comfortable. Around the same time, the Victor and Rover bicycle manufacturers introduced the familiar diamond-shaped, or double triangle, frame design common to most modern bicycles.

At the beginning of the twentieth century, the automobile was invented. The bicycle soon fell out of favor in the developed world. Bikes enjoyed renewed popularity in the 1960s when people became concerned about their physical fitness and automobile pollution. The basic mechanics of the bicycle have changed very little over the years, although design changes have

▲ Some of the most recent developments in bicycle technology, such as front and rear suspension and hydraulic disc brakes, have been incorporated into the design of mountain bikes.

made cycling far safer and more efficient. High-tech, lightweight materials are now commonly used to make sturdy mountain bikes, two-person tandems, compact folding bikes, and professional racing machines.

Wheeling along

The wheels are essential parts of all bicycles. They must be tough to support the weight of the cyclist and bear forces such as braking, pedaling, and the impact from moving along the ground. The wheels also need to be light to allow the bike to move with speed and efficiency.

Each wheel consists of a central hub, the rim, the spokes, and an inflatable tire. Most modern rims and spokes are made from aluminum or steel, but professional rims are made of high-tech materials such as carbon fiber. Plastic rims and spokes have also been developed, but their use is limited to BMX stunt bikes and childrens' bikes. The spokes connect the hub to the rim, usually in a crisscross pattern. Most rims are fitted with pneumatic tires. Pneumatic tires make for a comfortable ride, but they are liable to puncture on sharp objects such as broken glass. Racing and touring bikes have thin, smooth tires. Smooth tires are better for cycling on even surfaces such as roads. Mountain bikes have fat, knobbly (rough) tires to grip uneven surfaces such as dirt trails.

The frame

The frame consists of connected tubes that support the cyclist's weight and hold all the other parts of the bicycle together. The frame must be stiff so that all the pushing effort on the pedals transfers into a turning movement of the wheels. However, the frame must also have a little bit of "give" to smooth out bumpy roads or cycle paths. To achieve the desired combination of stiffness and flexibility, many different materials are used to make bicycle frames. Steel was once the material of choice, but aluminum and titanium alloys are becoming the industry standard. Professional racing frames are also made from materials such as carbon fiber to reduce the overall weight of the bicycle.

Bicycle gears

The problem with early bicycles was that they traveled only as far as one complete turn of the wheel for one complete turn of the pedals. To go faster, the front wheel could be up to 50 inches (130 centimeters) in diameter, while the rear wheel had a diameter of about 24 inches (60 centimeters). Every turn of the pedals turned the big wheel once, so the bike traveled farther for each turn.

Modern bikes have gears that change the amount the bike moves forward with each turn of the pedals. The gears at the front of the gear mechanism are called chainwheels. The chain links the chainwheels to the gears on the rear wheel, which are called the sprockets. Spring-loaded mechanisms called derailleurs move the chain from one gear to another. The front derailleur moves the chain between the chainwheels, while the rear derailleur moves the chain between the sprockets.

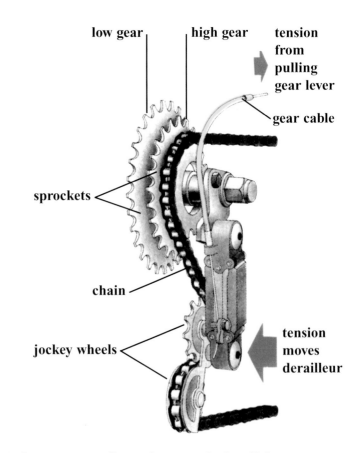

▲ *Pressing a small gear lever on the handlebars increases the tension in the gear cable. This moves the derailleur mechanism carrying the jockey wheels over the range of sprockets.*

◀ *U.S. BMX rider Rob Nolli performs a stunt at the 1999 Summer X Games in San Francisco. BMX cycling became popular in California in the 1970s. Over the years, more and more people have tuned into BMX.*

they do not work very well in wet weather. Water lubricates the wheel rims, making it difficult for pads to grip the rim.

Many mountain bikes are now fitted with hydraulic brakes. As the cyclist squeezes the brake levers, small pistons push against a special fluid inside narrow tubes leading to each wheel. There are two types of hydraulic brakes. With hydraulic disc brakes, the fluid clamps pads against a disc attached to the wheel. With drum brakes, the pads press against the inside of an enclosed drum. The drum forms part of the wheel hub. Hydraulic brakes are heavier than cable brakes, but they are a much more efficient way of slowing the bicycle.

On most bikes with derailleur gears, the cyclist changes gear by shifting gear levers on the handlebars. A cable connects the levers to the spring mechanism inside the derailleur.

Gears help cyclists achieve the best combination of pedaling effort and pedaling speed. A cyclist changes into low gear (small chainwheel and large sprocket) when riding uphill. Although this makes pedaling easier, the bicycle moves more slowly. On level surfaces, a cyclist changes to a high gear (large chainwheel and small sprocket), which makes pedaling slower but the bike go faster.

Slowing and stopping

The earliest bicycles did not have brakes, so cycling was dangerous. It soon became clear that bikes needed brakes to allow the cyclist to slow or stop. The most popular brake system is the cable-operated caliper brake. To slow or stop the bike, the cyclist pulls brake levers on the handlebars. The levers tighten cables running from the lever to brake arms either side of each wheel rim. As the cable tightens, it pulls the arms together, clamping brake pads tightly against the rim. Cable-operated disc brakes work in the same way, but they clamp brake pads onto metal discs attached to the wheels. Cable brakes are light, inexpensive, and strong, but

DID YOU KNOW?

The world's smallest bicycle was built by Charlie Charles and ridden by him in a Las Vegas cabaret act. Each wheel measured 2⅛ inches (5.4 centimeters) across.

Suspension systems

Many modern mountain bikes are fitted with front and rear suspension systems. The suspension moves up and down to smooth the ride over very bumpy roads and dirt trails. The suspension also lets cyclists land from huge jumps without damaging the frame. Suspension systems consist of a spring and an oil-filled damper. The spring moves up and down to absorb bumps in the road. The damper discharges energy stored in the spring through the oil, which stops the suspension from bouncing out of control. The front suspension is inside the front forks. The forks move up when the bike hits a bump. The design of rear suspension systems varies from one manufacturer to the next.

See also: BRAKE SYSTEM • SUSPENSION • WHEEL

Biochemistry

Biochemistry is the chemistry of life. It studies the chemical compounds and processes that occur in living organisms such as animals and plants.

Biochemists study the chemical reactions that keep animals and plants alive. Every animal needs food, air, and water to survive. These are the building blocks that provide raw materials for the processes of life. In a similar way, plants need sunlight, air, water, and nutrients from the soil for them to flourish.

Digestion

When people eat, food must be broken down into a form the body can use. Digestion begins as soon as food enters the mouth. Teeth chew food into small pieces, and the saliva contains an enzyme, called amylase, to help break down carbohydrates in food. The stomach continues the digestive process. It secretes digestive juices that contain hydrochloric acid (HCl) and pepsin. Pepsin is another enzyme.

Digestion breaks down large chainlike protein molecules into small amino acid molecules, and it breaks down fats into fatty acids. Some carbohydrates break down to form simple sugars. Other carbohydrates pass through the digestive system intact. Dieticians call these carbohydrates dietary fiber. Amino acids, fatty acids, and simple sugars are small enough to pass through the membrane that forms the walls of the digestive system and into the bloodstream. The products of digestion then circulate in the bloodstream until they are picked up by cells.

DID YOU KNOW?

Most plants contain a green pigment called chlorophyll, which they use to collect energy from sunlight during photosynthesis. Chlorophyll is such an intense green that it is used to color soaps and cosmetics. Synthetic chemicals with structures similar to chlorophyll have been produced in a wide range of colors for use as pigments.

◄ Plants such as this sunflower use energy from sunlight to convert carbon dioxide and water into food and oxygen. This process, known as photosynthesis, consists of a complex series of biochemical reactions. Photosynthesis provides plants with the energy needed for growth and development.

Metabolism

Cells are surrounded by a membrane composed of protein and fat molecules. Cells contain fluid, proteins, and molecules such as deoxyribonucleic acid (DNA; the molecule that contains the genetic code). Cells make up all the tissues in almost all living organisms. Some proteins in cells are enzymes that process the products of digestion in a series of biochemical reactions called metabolism.

One set of metabolic reactions breaks down sugars into carbon dioxide gas (CO_2), water, and energy. Some of this energy keeps warm-blooded animals warm and gives them strength. The rest drives other metabolic reactions, such as protein synthesis. Protein synthesis assembles proteins from strings of amino acids according to the genetic code contained in DNA. The human body uses this process to create proteins from other proteins in food. The human body can make all but eight of the 26 different amino acids that form proteins. The rest are the essential amino acids, which are obtained from food. Cells store spare energy as fat molecules, so people who eat more food energy than they use become overweight.

The metabolic rate also depends on the levels of hormones in the body. These form in glands and travel through the bloodstream to cells all over the body. Hormones from the thyroid gland in the neck govern how quickly metabolism converts food energy. A lack of these hormones can make people tired and lacking in energy.

Disease and drugs

Illnesses can occur because a person's lifestyle fails to provide all the nutrients needed for good health. An example is rickets, in which bones soften and deform. Rickets is a deficiency disease. Too little calcium in the diet can cause rickets, as can lack of exposure to sunlight, which keeps the body from producing vitamin D. Another deficiency disease is scurvy, which is caused by a lack of vitamin C in the diet. Biochemists have found that dietary supplements can prevent most deficiency diseases.

Sometimes normal biochemical reactions in the body go wrong. In one form of diabetes, the body fails to produce enough insulin—an enzyme that uses sugars to produce energy. From biochemistry, doctors know to test for glucose in blood and urine to monitor diabetes. Injections of insulin help diabetics live normal lives.

See also: AMINO ACID • CELL • DIGESTIVE SYSTEM • DNA • ENZYME • FAT • PROTEIN

▶ *A biochemist searches for genetic mutations in samples of human blood. Color differences on the computer screen indicate the presence or absence of the mutations. The study of biochemistry is important to medicine. Understanding the chemical reactions that cause disease helps in diagnosis and treatment.*

Biodiversity

The astounding variety of life on the planet is expressed as Earth's biodiversity. Biodiversity is driven and controlled by the formation and extinction of species and can fluctuate widely over time. Due to human activities, biodiversity is currently undergoing a very rapid decline.

Many different types, or species, of organisms live in Earth's varied biomes and habitats. Some places are teeming with wildlife, but only a small fraction of the total range of organisms may be apparent to passersby. In a local park, for example, trees, grasses, and other plants will be visible. A few types of large vertebrates (animals with backbones), such as birds, squirrels, and maybe even snakes and deer, might be seen. However, there will also be vast numbers of invertebrates (animals without backbones). Some, such as aphids, feed on the plants. Others, such as ants and spiders, eat other invertebrates. Many organisms exist that feed on dead or decaying matter—earthworms in the soil and fungi and young beetles inside dead wood. Finally, there will

▲ *Tropical rain forests, such as this one in the Amazon basin in Brazil, contain the greatest diversity of species on the surface of Earth.*

◄ *A rock python swallows an impala in Kenya. Sustaining a balance between predators and prey is crucial to Earth's biodiversity.*

be countless millions of tiny creatures, such as bacteria and protists, living in the soil or as parasites inside other creatures.

Biodiversity varies greatly around the world. Although a park may contain hundreds or even thousands of different species, this diversity will be dwarfed by that of a similarly sized patch of tropical rain forest. Climatic conditions in the rain forest are the most favorable for life. The size of an area also affects biodiversity. For example, large islands are generally more biodiverse than small islands. Biodiversity also depends on other factors, such as climate, vegetation, and human activities.

How many species exist on Earth?

The term *biodiversity* was coined by U.S. entomologist (insect specialist) Edward O. Wilson (1929–) in 1986. Since then, biodiversity has been cited as a priority of many conservation groups around the world. However, it is difficult to figure out just how biodiverse Earth really is. Almost two million different species of organisms have been named, but scientists have a very long way to go until every species on Earth has been found, described, and cataloged. Some think there may be 10 million insect species alone, while other estimates suggest there may be more than 100 million species of organisms in total.

How do biologists define a species?

A species is usually defined as a group of organisms that can interbreed only with each other. However, many organisms defy this explanation. Most species of bacteria do not reproduce by exchanging genes. Instead, they reproduce by "budding" into two new individuals. This is called asexual reproduction. Some species may interbreed and produce hybrids. A mule is a hybrid of a horse and a donkey. Most animal hybrids are unable to reproduce. Many plant hybrids can breed, however, forming new species after just one breeding. Crops such as corn are hybrid species. Biologists also recognize different forms, called subspecies, within the same species. Most subspecies crop up as a result of geographical isolation within a species. Biologists recognize 24 subspecies of gray wolf in North America, for example, each one classified according to the geographical area in which it lives. Biologists have expanded the definition of biodiversity to take these issues into account, giving a truer reflection of life's diversity. Earth's biodiversity is now defined as the total diversity of species, subspecies, ecosystems, and genes.

DID YOU KNOW?

The presence of cryptic species can lead to an underestimate of an area's biodiversity. Cryptic species are pairs or groups of species that look identical to human eyes and can be separated only by detailed behavioral or genetic studies. In 1996, for example, biologists in England realized that what was believed to be one species of common bat, the pipistrelle, was actually two different species. One of the cryptic species, now called the soprano pipistrelle, can be distinguished only by the higher frequency of the sound pulses it uses to find its way around and hunt at night.

How do species form?

Scientists think that the earliest microorganisms appeared around 3.5 billion years ago. Since then, billions of species have appeared, flourished, and become extinct. How does such biodiversity arise? New types of organisms form through a process called speciation, in which one species gradually turns into two or more new species.

When genes are passed from parent to young, they may contain mistakes called mutations. Many mutations are harmful, and the young offspring die without reproducing. Sometimes a mutation can be beneficial. It will help the organism survive and produce lots of young that will also have the beneficial mutation. In time, organisms with the mutation will completely replace those without it, since they have a higher chance of surviving to produce young. This is called natural selection, and it is the driving force behind evolution.

Imagine a population of finches living on the coast of South America. Due to natural selection, small populations of the finches adapt to local conditions, but there is regular migration between the populations. This movement leads to a constant mixing of genes, called gene flow. Now, imagine that a pair of finches is blown away during a fierce storm and eventually lands, exhausted, on a small

► *The climate varies dramatically in mountain environments. As a result, species with very different specializations can be found in these regions.*

island hundreds of miles offshore. Gene flow between these finches' descendants and those on the mainland is now impossible. Without gene flow, mutations that help the finches adapt to changes in the environment develop unchecked. Another effect, called genetic drift, also becomes important. Genetic drift is the random loss of certain genes over the generations. In large populations, these losses tend to cancel out. In small populations, such as the finches on the island, they can become more widespread.

Isolation and adaptation

Isolated from the rest of the finch population, the island finches evolve to suit their habitat over time. Eventually, the genetic differences between the two finch groups are great enough that breeding cannot take place between them—they can now be said to be separate species. There may be many factors that keep newly formed species from breeding besides their geographical separation. For example, the island finches may sing in a way that does not attract females of the mainland race. Factors such as these are called isolating mechanisms.

Biologists think that a scenario like this took place on the Galápagos Islands, where 14 species of finches live, all probably descended from a single pair of finches from mainland South America.

Speciation occurs over vast timescales and has never been directly observed. However, most biologists think it must have happened on billions of occasions, both today and in the past, to account for Earth's incredible biodiversity. The rate at which new species form is not constant, however. In an environment free of competition between different organisms, speciation can occur very quickly. In a few hundred thousand years, the descendants of those first finches on the Galápagos Islands evolved into different species, each adapted to fill a specific ecological role, or niche. The finches are similar in size and color, but there is great diversity in characteristics such as bill shape.

Changes in Earth's biodiversity

The biodiversity of an area can fluctuate wildly with time. In North America, for example, biodiversity was low during the last ice age but increased as the glaciers retreated. Around 12,000 years ago, however, the biodiversity of the continent dipped sharply. This may have been due to the arrival of the ancestors of Native Americans, or it may have been due to climate change. Either way, within a few thousand years most of the larger animals were extinct. Global biodiversity can also vary widely. At the end of the Permian period (around 250 million years ago), for example, around 97 percent of all life on Earth was wiped out in a mass extinction. Another mass extinction at the end of the Cretaceous period (65 million years ago) saw the demise of the dinosaurs, among other groups. Following a mass extinction, the survivors undergo a period of rapid speciation, filling niches in the absence of competition.

Human impact on biodiversity

Ever since people began to control their environment, by using fire to clear forests and planting crops instead, Earth's biodiversity has been in decline. This process has accelerated over the last one hundred years at an alarming rate, as tropical forests have been cut down, oceans overfished, and grasslands replaced by fields of crops. Today, at least 60,000 species are in imminent danger of

◄ *The world's oceans are some of the most biodiverse areas on Earth. So far, people have discovered only a fraction of the millions of different species living in the oceans. However, overfishing and other commercial activities have reduced many of these species to the brink of extinction.*

▶ *Protesters march at the 1992 Earth Summit in Rio de Janeiro, Brazil. The human impact on Earth's biodiversity is a concern for many people.*

extinction. Thousands more species are lost every year before biologists get a chance to classify them. If the current rate of destruction continues, up to 15 percent of Earth's biodiversity will be lost by 2020 and up to 25 percent by 2025.

Extinction of just a single species can have wide-reaching implications for the biodiversity of an area. Imagine that jaguars were hunted to extinction. Their demise would spell doom for jaguar parasites, such as fleas and lice. The bacteria that live inside the jaguars would become extinct,

DID YOU KNOW?

Rather than trying to save every endangered species, some biologists think that the most practical way to conserve biodiversity is to focus on 25 "biodiversity hot spots." These are areas, such as Costa Rica, Madagascar, and the Philippines, that are particularly rich in species and must be saved at all costs.

too. The loss of the big cat may also have indirect consequences. There may be a boom in the population of smaller prey animals, and so the species on which these animals feed could also suffer serious decline.

Why worry about biodiversity?

The world's biodiversity is a vast resource, providing food and energy, as well as materials such as rubber and cotton. Much of this resource remains untapped, however. The rain forests may contain plants with genes that could be transplanted into crops to provide protection against pests. Other plants may contain chemicals that could cure diseases. The Madagascar periwinkle plant, for example, contains a drug that dramatically increases the survival chances of a patient with leukemia. As species become extinct at an ever-increasing rate, more of these important resources are lost to science forever.

See also: BIOLOGY • BIOMES AND HABITATS

Biology

Biology is the science of life. There are many different branches of biology. Some biologists look at the chemical processes that go on inside cells. Others study fossils to explain how different organisms evolved. Still others explore the relationships different plants and animals have with their environment.

The word *biology* comes from the Greek words *bios,* which means "life," and *logos,* meaning "study." Biologists study living organisms and life processes, including evolution, genetics, growth and development, origin, and structure.

The history of biology

The first person to use the word *biology* to describe the science of life was German scientist Gottfried Reinhold Treviranus (1776–1837) in his book *Biologie, oder Philosophie de Lebended Natur für Naturforscher und Aerzte* (Biology, or the Philosophy of Living Nature for Natural Scientists and Physicians), which he wrote between 1802 and 1822. However, the ancient Greeks were the first to study living organisms in detail. In the fourth century BCE, Greek philosopher and scientist Aristotle (384–322 BCE) came up with a system for

▼ *Two girls study bird life from a bed of reeds. Birding is the fastest-growing outdoor activity in the United States. A recent survey by the U.S. Fish and Wildlife Service indicated that more than 50 million Americans go out to watch birds in their natural habitat.*

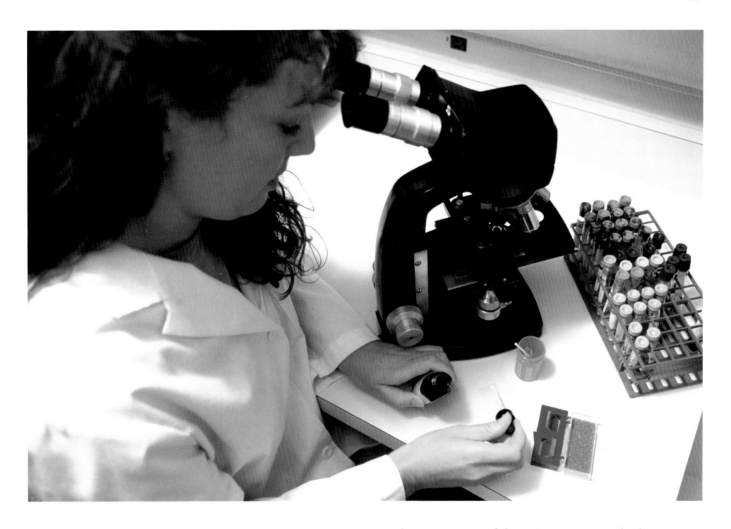

▲ *A biologist prepares a slide for viewing under a light microscope. Microscopy opened up a whole new world to biologists, enabling the observation of biological processes at the cellular level. In fact, modern microscopes are so powerful that biologists can even study processes inside cells at the molecular level.*

classifying animal species by comparing similarities in body structure. Theophrastus (371–286 BCE), a student of Aristotle, presented a similar system for classifying many plant species.

There were few major advances in biology until the Renaissance in Europe between the fourteenth and seventeenth centuries CE. The science of anatomy emerged thanks in large part to Belgian physician Andreas Vesalius (1514–1564) and his book *De Humani Corporis Fabrica Libri Septem* (The Seven Books on the Structure of the Human Body), published in 1543. Similarly, modern physiology owes a great deal to the work of English physician William Harvey (1578–1657).

The invention of the microscope at the beginning of the seventeenth century revolutionized the study of biology. For the first time, scientists observed simple, single-celled organisms such as bacteria and protists. The microscope also revealed that most animals plants and animals consist of tiny units called cells. Many more advances in the biological sciences were made as microscopes became increasingly powerful.

One of the most important contributions to biology in the eighteenth century was made by Swedish botanist and physician Carolus Linnaeus (1707–1778). Linnaeus introduced a system for classifying and naming organisms by establishing the standard hierarchy of species, genus, order, and class. He also provided classification keys in his books, allowing scientists to identify animals and plants for themselves. Linnaeus's system is still the basis for naming animals and plants, which is testament to the importance of his work.

The evolution revolution

In 1858, British naturalists Charles Darwin (1809–1882) and Alfred Russel Wallace (1823–1913) announced the concepts of natural selection and evolution to explain the enormous diversity of life on Earth. The two scientists had independently arrived at the same conclusion that all living species are descended from simple ancestors who lived in the past. New species form and others die out as they adapt to changes in the world around them. The theory of evolution by natural selection was very controversial. It challenged the creationist idea that all species had been created by God, as described in the Bible.

The theory of evolution gradually came to be accepted as more and more evidence came to light. The fossil record indicated to biologists that animals change gradually as time passes. Another important discovery was made by Austrian monk and botanist Gregor Mendel (1822–1884). For natural selection to occur, Darwin and Wallace recognized that characteristics must pass from parent to offspring. Mendel proposed the idea of

▼ *A boy looks at dinosaur skeletons and eggs on display at the American Museum of Natural History in New York. By studying the fossilized remains of these ancient creatures, biologists can figure out how the reptiles might have lived.*

▲ *A biologist examines a genetic fingerprint from samples taken from a crime scene. Almost all cells in the human body carry genetic information in the form of molecules of deoxyribonucleic acid (DNA). A genetic fingerprint is an image of short sequences of bases within the DNA molecule. Apart from identical twins, the exact sequence of bases varies between individuals. The DNA found at a crime scene can, therefore, be matched to DNA taken from a suspected criminal.*

genes (then called particles) as the units of heredity. His work laid the foundations for rapid advances in evolution, genetics, and molecular biology.

Branches of biology

At one time, biologists studied either plants or animals, and biology was divided simply into botany and zoology. Today, the scope of biology is so diverse that most biologists specialize in a particular field. Some biologists consider problems at the molecular level, while others look at processes at the level of ecosystems. Some biologists limit their research to one group of organisms. For example, ichthyologists study fish, entomologists study insects, and ornithologists study birds. Other biologists study life processes such as growth and development (embryology and developmental biology) or body function (physiology). As biologists come up with new ideas and discoveries, the biological revolution will continue.

See also: ANIMAL KINGDOM • BACTERIA • BOTANY • PLANT KINGDOM • ZOOLOGY

Biomes and habitats

The words *biome* and *habitat* describe the natural environment of living things. A biome is a major geographical region, with a distinctive climate, plants, and animals. An organism's habitat is the type of place in which it lives.

Many aspects of an organism's surroundings affect its survival. Every animal and plant has features that suit it to the conditions in which it lives. Equipped with these features, an organism thrives in its own habitat, but it does not do so well in other habitats. In this sense, a habitat is what an organism needs for survival.

On land, the weather, including the temperature, wind, and moisture, usually decides whether a habitat is suitable for an organism. The amount of light can also be important, and so can the soil and terrain. In watery habitats, the speed of the water flow often plays a part, as well as the saltiness, temperature, and light levels in the water. A habitat is made up of all these elements, but it also includes the effects of the creatures living in the habitat. Some organisms are sources of food, while others are competitors in the fight for survival. Still others are predators. Some organisms, such as trees, provide a platform, a place of safety, or somewhere to make a home. Neighboring organisms are crucial elements in a creature's habitat. Scientists try to consider all these aspects when describing a habitat.

Habitats are unique to each organism

In a strict sense, a habitat is the type of place a particular organism lives in. Each type of organism, or species, has its own habitat. To see that this is true, think of a maple woodland. It might seem to be one habitat. In fact, it contains many different habitats. In the treetops—in the continuous layer of leafy branches called the canopy—there is a habitat for squirrels. They leap among the thin branches, collecting seeds and nuts. However, they cannot reach the flimsiest twigs. Small perching birds hunt on these twigs, picking off insects in a habitat where squirrels never go. Within the leaves themselves, tiny insect larvae dig tunnels as they eat the leaves from the inside. For these larvae, their habitat is the inside of a leaf. On the tree trunks, beetles live in crevices in the bark. To these beetles, the habitat is a landscape of bark. Down in the soil, there are more habitats. Even creatures themselves are habitats for organisms. Creatures called parasites live on or inside other organisms. For example, a tapeworm's habitat might be a deer's intestines.

The world's biomes

It is rarely possible to look at habitats in such detail. On the largest scale, people divide Earth into major geographical regions called biomes. Biomes include

▶ *The seashore provides plants and animals with several challenges, including pounding waves and salt-laden winds. Shifting sands provide little anchorage for roots, and food is often scattered and hard to find.*

the animals and plants that live in the habitat. Each biome is recognizable because it has characteristic biodiversity. The climate, or the pattern of weather over an average year, is also distinctive and helps define the biome. A biome's plant life is made up of plants that thrive in the biome's particular climate. The climate and plant life together shape the biome's characteristic animal life. For example, the taiga biome in the Northern Hemisphere has a cool, wet climate. The vegetation there consists mainly of forests of cone-bearing trees such as firs, pines, and spruces. Animals that thrive in the taiga include birds such as woodpeckers and owls and mammals such as caribou and wolves. Taiga is very different from other biomes, such as desert or shrubland.

Biomes are broad categories, and there are only a few of them on Earth. Some biomes cover vast areas of Earth's land surface, while others are underwater. The categories are not perfect. Biologists still argue about how different biomes should be classified.

▼ *Major land biomes occur in broad bands around the world or in large patches that correspond to different types of climate—hot and dry, warm and wet, or cool and variable. In contrast, the river and lake and wetland biomes are hardly visible because they are scattered in many small bodies of water in every continent. Oceans include several biomes.*

> ### DID YOU KNOW?
> Deserts form the largest terrestrial (land) biome. They cover more than 25 percent of Earth's land surface.

Arctic tundra and polar desert

In the far north of Asia, Europe, and North America is a region of permanently frozen soil. The average temperature in summer rises little above 50°F (10°C), but it can drop to –40°F (–40°C) in winter. Although the topsoil melts each year, the underlying soil remains frozen. The frozen soil, called permafrost, prevents roots from tapping deep into the ground. The biome created is a treeless plain called arctic tundra. This is different from the tundra on high mountains in other regions. It does not have this layer of permafrost. Tundra on mountains is called alpine tundra.

The brief tundra summer is a sudden flurry of flowering plants and hordes of buzzing insects. The only creatures that remain active throughout the year are warm-blooded mammals and birds. Most of these animals migrate south each winter. The few that stay, such as marmots and ptarmigans, survive by eating plants beneath the snow.

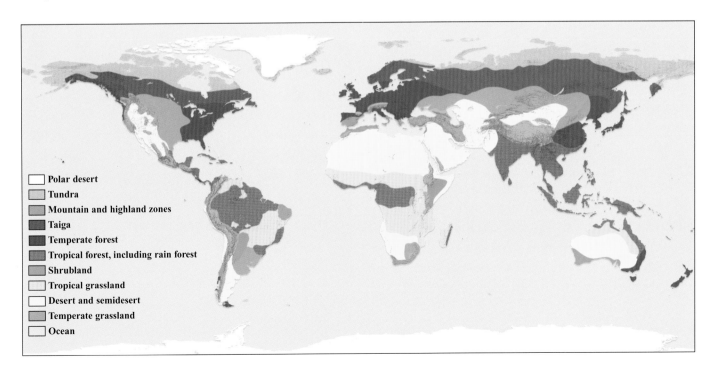

- [ ] Polar desert
- Tundra
- Mountain and highland zones
- Taiga
- Temperate forest
- Tropical forest, including rain forest
- Shrubland
- Tropical grassland
- Desert and semidesert
- Temperate grassland
- Ocean

◀ *Few creatures can survive in the polar desert. One animal that does is the polar bear. It survives by hunting seals in the surrounding waters.*

It does not snow often in arctic tundra, and some places are very dry and barren. Some experts regard these places as a separate biome called polar desert. Polar desert occurs in the Antarctic and in the high Arctic. The dry, polar desert is so cold that ice rarely melts, and it builds up into thick sheets.

Taiga

South of the arctic tundra, the climate allows trees to take hold, creating the taiga biome, or northern coniferous forest. The taiga is an almost continuous belt of cone-bearing, needle-leaved trees stretching around the northern continents. There is more rain and snow in the taiga than in the arctic tundra, and the summers are warmer. In the center of continents, however, taiga winters can be even colder. Temperatures in eastern Siberia can drop below –58°F (–50°C). Apart from extreme cold, taiga trees endure long periods without water each winter because water in the soil is frozen. The trees have small, needlelike leaves to protect them from water loss. The taiga is mainly evergreen. The trees do not lose their leaves in the fall, and their leaves are ready to begin absorbing water and making food the moment the soil water melts in spring. Most taiga animals either migrate or hibernate through the harsh winter. If they stay active, many animals, such as arctic hares, grow white coats.

▶ *Taiga forests contain evergreen coniferous trees. These can survive the freezing taiga winters.*

Temperate forest

In the south of the taiga belt, the climate becomes increasingly mild. The winters are not very cold, and the summers are never particularly hot. Such a climate is called temperate, and the forest biome that develops there is called temperate forest. The taiga merges in the south with the temperate forest which, until the last 1,000 to 2,000 years, covered much of Europe, China, Japan, and eastern North America. Today, people have destroyed most of Earth's temperate forests to create farmland.

The plant life of most temperate forests is composed of broad-leaved trees that shed their leaves in the fall. Broad leaves capture more of the Sun's energy than needlelike leaves, but frost damages them. The temperate winter is mild but still features many nights of frost. The longer growing season of the temperate climate allows time for new leaves to unfurl each spring.

Temperate forest animals must cope with the yearly cycle of leaf shedding and growing. Since there is far less plant food available in winter, some animals hibernate and some migrate to warmer regions. Still others survive on stored nuts and seeds.

Temperate grasslands

Grassland develops in regions that have a temperate climate but receive less than 20 inches (50 centimeters) of rainfall every year. These grasslands form the temperate grassland biome, which covers central North America and extends across eastern Europe and central Asia and parts of Argentina, South Africa, and southern Australia. Since these grasslands often occupy the center of continents, the weather can often be extreme, even though the climate is temperate. Winters can be very cold and summers very hot. Most animal life is found underground in burrows, sheltered from the wind, cold, and predators. Burrowing rodents, such as prairie dogs, are abundant in grasslands. Animals tend to be nocturnal (active at night) to avoid predators. The temperate grassland climate is ideal for some of our favorite crops, including the grasses corn and wheat. People have transformed most of Earth's temperate grassland into farmland.

Tropical grasslands

Grasslands in hot countries make up a separate biome called tropical grassland. The climate that creates them is much wetter, but since the hot, tropical sunshine dries the land more quickly, more rain is needed to sustain forests. Rains in tropical grasslands also come unevenly throughout the year. Although there may be more than 48 inches (120 centimeters) of rain a year, there may be one or two wet seasons of intense rainfall with periods of low rainfall in between. Tropical grassland supports a great diversity and abundance of large, plant-eating animals, from small antelope to elephants. The plant eaters, in turn, feed a variety of meat-eating animals such as hyenas and lions.

Desert and shrubland

A desert is any region with less than 10 inches (25 centimeters) of rainfall a year. Plants usually form a sparse cover, and they are specialized in various ways to get water and retain it. On the margins of deserts, the climate is less harsh and allows different plant life to grow. Near some hot deserts, tough, drought-resistant shrubs form part of the shrubland biome. The shrubland biome occurs in scattered patches around Earth, including the Mediterranean coastal region and much of California. Although shrubland usually experiences periods of low rainfall in summer, many localities enjoy a pleasant, warm climate.

▶ *The African savanna is a tropical grassland, scattered with trees and shrubs. Giraffes are well adapted to the savanna, browsing on leaves high in the treetops.*

▲ *The Florida Everglades make up a huge wetland. The trees that live there are adapted to survive with their roots constantly underwater. Animal inhabitants include alligators and a wide range of fish.*

Tropical forest

The biome lying either side of the equator is called tropical forest. Tropical forest is supported by abundant yearly rainfall of more than 100 inches (250 centimeters). The rain falls throughout the year in equatorial rain forest, but in most tropical forests there is a marked dry season during which much less rain falls. In the type of tropical forest called monsoon forest, there is such a long dry season each year that the trees lose their leaves and remain leafless for a period to save water. Other tropical forest has lush leaves all year long. The tall trees create a complex, three-dimensional environment where a huge variety of plants and animals live in different, small habitats from the canopy down to the soil. There is no other land biome so rich in species.

Like temperate forest, the tropical forest biome is being destroyed by people. The land does not make good farmland, but the trees are felled for timber and cleared during mineral exploration.

Rivers, lakes, and wetlands

There is a huge range of different habitats in bodies of freshwater—lakes, ponds, rivers, streams, and wetlands. You could say there are several biomes present, but most scientists describe just three. The first is made up of rivers and streams. Most rivers and streams are fast-flowing bodies of freshwater. They support a wide range of animals and plants.

The second biome consists of lakes and ponds. Not all the habitats in the lake and pond biome are freshwater. Some lakes are salty, some saltier than the ocean, and some are full of other dissolved chemicals. These cause contrasting conditions and problems for the creatures living in them.

The third biome is made up of wetlands, which includes bogs, fens, marshes, and swamps, including mangrove swamps. Some wetlands, such as bogs and sometimes fens, have no standing water. These wetlands are composed only of waterlogged soil. If wetlands have standing water, it is generally shallow enough for plants to emerge and grow high above the water surface.

The ocean

The oceans cover two-thirds of Earth's surface to an average depth of 2.5 miles (4 kilometers). They are composed of many different biomes, from sunlit coral reefs to ocean trenches 6 miles (10 kilometers) deep. At the margins of the oceans, coastal areas such as beaches, cliffs, and mudflats form the boundary between the ocean's biomes and land biomes. Although animals and other terrestrial and ocean life-forms live around coasts, the shore between high tide and low tide is a major type of habitat in its own right. It is called the intertidal zone. In some classifications, beaches and coasts are considered to be a separate biome.

Mountains

Mountains and highlands pose a tricky problem for scientists trying to classify Earth's biomes. Conditions are completely different at the top of a mountain compared to halfway up, being much colder and windier at the top. The climate might be warm and wet on one mountain slope, but hot and

▲ *Mountains contain a wide range of biomes in a small area. In this picture alone, grassland, taiga, and polar desert can be seen clearly.*

dry on the opposite side. Mountain ranges are complex mosaics of small biomes. Ecologists prefer to describe mountains and highlands as systems instead of as a single biome.

Shortcomings of the biome concept

Biomes are convenient categories, but they do not reflect nature's true complexity. For every boundary between two biomes, there are places that fall in between instead of fitting neatly into one category or another. A biome is a broad, global concept, and it encompasses a great deal of variation. Temperate forest, for example, is a single biome, but it might be deciduous (with trees losing their leaves in fall), such as the woodland of New England, or frost free, well watered, and evergreen, such as the temperate rain forest of New Zealand. The temperate forest of the Pacific Northwest, on the other hand, is also very moist all year round but contains evergreen, needle-leaved trees. Some people group this temperate forest as part of the taiga biome. There is seldom agreement between experts about the exact distinction between biomes.

Human interference

Defining biomes is even harder because of the influence of people. The effect of people is drastic in the case of draining or poisoning wetlands or felling trees and forest to make farmland. The result in these cases can be a change from a forest biome to different kinds of artificial grassland, serving as pastureland or cropland. Human interference can be more subtle, however. Most scientists think that the shrubland biome around the Mediterranean coast has been shaped partly by thousands of years of grazing by goats herded by people. Without the goats, the biome might be similar to the temperate, deciduous woodland in more central parts of Europe. Grazing in marginal desert areas also changes dry shrubland or grassland into artificial desert.

Like the animals and plants in them, biomes are changing all the time due to evolution and changing influences such as human interference and climate change. It is sometimes difficult to identify where biomes begin and end, but that is because scientists' categories are simple compared to nature's complexity.

▲ *This dam across the Mississippi River has created an artificial lake. By changing the landscape, people directly affect natural habitats and biomes.*

See also: AGRICULTURE • ECOLOGY • FOOD WEB

Biorhythm

Many people who have to get up at a certain time every morning wake up just before the alarm goes off. There seems to be a mysterious clock in the brain that wakes them up at just the right time. This is a "biological clock," and it is worked by biorhythms.

People's lives are constantly affected by the world in which they live. Earth rotates on its axis once every day, giving us periods of light and darkness. The seasons change as Earth orbits (revolves around) the Sun. Changes in air pressure, light, and temperature go on all the time, and people may hardly notice them.

Along with all animals and plants, people have become used to a 24-hour cycle. Scientists call this cycle the circadian rhythm. Generally, people are only aware of the most obvious circadian rhythm—sleeping and being awake. However, there are many other body processes that vary at certain times during the day and night. For example, breathing rate, blood pressure, body temperature, pulse rate, and many other life processes vary in time with the invisible human biological clock. In fact, people can stay healthy only if all these body rhythms work together.

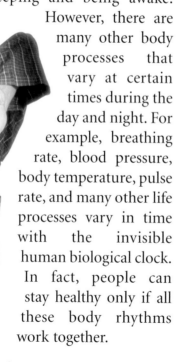

Morning and afternoon people

Body rhythms vary from one person to the next. Some people like to get up early and do their best work in the morning. Others have difficulty waking up and work best later in the day. This seems to have something to do with body temperature. Each day a person's temperature rises and falls regularly by two or three degrees. These temperature changes always happen at the same time of day. For a person who sleeps at night, their highest body temperature is usually in the late afternoon or evening. This period of high temperature is usually the person's favorite time of day.

A person's lowest temperature occurs while they sleep, and it rises as they approach the time when they have to get up. People who are bright and active when they first get up usually have a temperature rise that happens earlier than normal. Those who awaken slowly and have difficulty getting up have a temperature cycle that is just beginning to rise at the time when they get up.

Pulse rate seems to follow body temperature. Pulse rate also rises to its highest rate during the afternoon and slows during the night.

Other things change regularly during the circadian 24-hour rhythm. Some glands work better at certain times of the day. When the glands work harder, people feel more active. When they slow down, people feel tired and lazy.

Even the rate at which the kidneys make urine varies throughout the day. When people are asleep they make very little urine, so they seldom have to go to the bathroom during the night.

The senses change

Some of the senses have rhythms, too. The senses of hearing, smell, and taste are usually at their most acute between 5:00 PM and 7:00 PM. This is the time

◀ *People who wake up feeling tired have a lower body temperature in the mornings than those who wake feeling alert. Body temperature rises and falls according to a daily rhythm, which is different for every individual.*

of day when most people usually enjoy stimulating activities best, such as eating, drinking, and listening to music.

Constant rhythms

To see whether body rhythms can be made to change, people have lived for up to six months in deep caves kept at a constant temperature with around-the-clock artificial light. In these unnatural conditions, the body still keeps to its 24-hour rhythms. With time, however, and with nothing to check the body's clock, the average person's body systems will gradually creep toward a 25-hour day.

Some things can upset the body's rhythms. If a person changes from day to night shifts at work or goes on a long plane flight, the internal clock

▲ *Some creatures, such as this dormouse, hibernate through the winter months to save energy. Biorhythms tell these creatures when to start eating more to put on fat, as well as when to go into hibernation.*

becomes confused. If a person flies from Los Angeles to London, his or her body will become 11 hours out of sync. The person may have a meeting at 11:00 AM London time, but his or her internal clock will think it is midnight Los Angeles time. He or she would normally be going to bed.

Scientists think that the body adjusts to this "jet lag" at a rate of about one hour a day. It would therefore take a person about 11 days to adjust after a flight from Los Angeles to London. Studies of airline pilots and flight attendants who travel across many time zones have shown that some of their body functions can become very irregular.

Other body rhythms

The daily 24-hour body rhythm is only one of the rhythms of life. There are also monthly, seasonal, and yearly cycles. The most obvious of these is the female menstrual cycle. This biorhythm affects a woman's physical and emotional state at monthly intervals. These effects can, in some women, include changes in breathing rate, sight, and likelihood of catching infections. Some scientists think that men can also have monthly rhythms in which their moods change in a regular cycle.

Scientists also think that a gland called the thyroid gland produces a "summer hormone" that helps to reduce body temperature. Somehow the gland produces this hormone just before the hot summer months.

Animals and plants

Animals and plants use their body clocks in many ways. It is important to a bat in a dark cave or a scorpion in a hole to know that the Sun has set and that it is time for them to go outside and find food. Bees use their internal clocks when they go to find food, too. They tend to visit the same flowers at exactly the same time, day after day. Botanists have also found that some flowers produce most of their nectar at a particular time of the day. Over time, the bee and the flower may have synchronized their body clocks. The bees always come to the nectar supply, so there is a greater chance that the flowers will be pollinated.

▲ *Biorhythms tell salmon when to begin their migration from the sea to rivers to breed. The biorhythms ensure that all of the salmon arrive and spawn together, giving their eggs a better chance of not being eaten.*

DID YOU KNOW?

Experiments have been carried out with people who were put into a hypnotic sleep. It was found that their biological clock would wake them up at a certain time to carry out a particular task, even while they were under hypnosis.

Zoologists think that hibernation in some animals is triggered by biorhythms. When the temperature drops below a certain level, as in the winter months, many reptiles enter hibernation. The low temperature may suppress the appetite of the reptile, which triggers the onset of hibernation. Other animals hibernate in response to shorter day length or a decreased food supply. Hibernation in hedgehogs varies at any time from the onset of winter, depending on food reserves and day length.

Normally, biological clocks do not have to be completely accurate. But a very accurate time sense is needed by birds and animals that migrate. It seems that animals may navigate by "sightings" of the Sun and stars. But the position of the Sun and stars is never fixed in the sky. The animal would need to know the exact time difference between one position and another to keep on course.

We need to know more

Several reasons have been suggested as to how the human body rhythm emerges. Babies do not appear to have any biorhythms during the first few weeks of their lives. They sleep and wake up at any time of day or night. It seems that they have to learn to do things by a 24-hour clock.

It is only since the early 1960s that scientists have been trying to find out about people's biorhythms. It now seems likely that what they are discovering about these mysterious internal clocks will play a much bigger part in the future in how doctors look at and treat the human body.

See also: ENDOCRINE SYSTEM • METABOLISM

Black hole

Black holes are regions in space where gravity is so strong that nothing, not even light, can escape. A black hole forms when a massive star explodes and shrinks until its mass squeezes into a point of infinite density. Black holes are invisible, but scientists have detected them as companions to stars and as huge masses in the centers of faraway galaxies.

▲ *A portrait of German astronomer Karl Schwarzschild taken around 1905. In 1916, Schwarzschild published a solution to Einstein's general theory of relativity, which modeled the existence of black holes.*

Black holes are objects in space that exert such a strong gravitational force that they suck up nearby matter, such as a planet or cloud of gases, and crush it to infinite density. In fact, the gravity is so strong that it can slow down time and stretch out space. Even light, which travels at a speed of 186,000 miles an hour (300,000 kilometers per hour), cannot escape the vast gravitational pull of these celestial objects. Consequently, black holes are invisible and can only be detected by the effects they have on nearby matter.

Black holes may seem more the subject of science fiction than fact, especially as no one has ever identified one with complete certainty. However, there is now a large body of evidence to suggest that black holes are a reality, confirming theories that have been held for over two hundred years.

A mathematical curiosity

The first person to suggest the possibility of black holes was British astronomer and geologist John Michell (1724–1793) in 1784. Michell suggested that the gravity of an object might be so great that nothing, not even light, could escape it. Michell realized that such an object, which he called a dark star, would have to be huge and phenomenally dense. French astronomer and mathematician Pierre-Simon de Laplace (1749–1827) included Michell's ideas in his 1796 guide to astronomy, but they were subsequently dropped from the third edition of the guide.

When German-born U.S. physicist Albert Einstein (1879–1955) presented his general theory of relativity in 1915, interest in black holes was revived. In 1916, German astronomer Karl Schwarzschild (1873–1916) used Einstein's theory to prove that black holes could exist. Einstein was critical of Schwarzschild's work. He believed that black holes were just a mathematical curiosity. In 1930, however, Indian-born U.S. astrophysicist Subrahmanyan Chandrasekhar (1910–1995) produced detailed calculations to prove that large

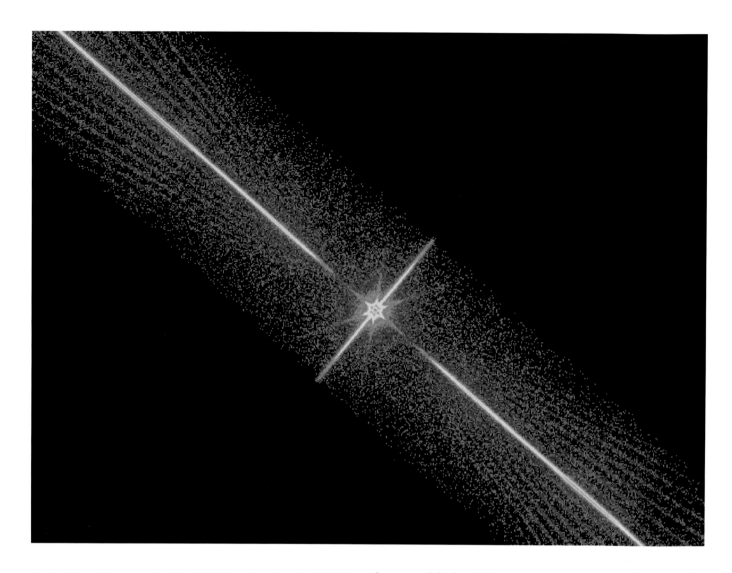

▲ *An X-ray image of a black hole taken by the NASA Chandra X-Ray Observatory. The gravitational force surrounding a black hole is so strong that it sucks up any matter that gets too close. This matter gets so hot that it emits pulses of X-ray radiation. Astronomers identify black holes by looking for these X-ray pulses.*

stars will finally collapse into frozen stars, as they were then called. In 1967, U.S. physicist John Wheeler (1911–) coined the term *black hole* for these dark, invisible voids.

Different black holes

Scientists think that there are three different types of black holes. They are the stellar-mass, galactic, and primordial black holes.

Stellar-mass black holes may result when a large star explodes in a supernova. Stars are giant balls of burning gases that generate enormous amounts of heat and light. When a star runs out of gases, the core collapses and the outer layers explode away. If the core is big enough, nothing can stop it from collapsing into a black hole. The force of gravity then becomes so strong that it bends space and slows down time. The space inside the black hole is so bent that it forms a spherical boundary in space called the event horizon. Nothing can escape from the event horizon—not even the light that the star continues to emit. Eventually, the mass of the star collapses into a singularity—a point of infinite density where all the laws of physics break down.

Galactic black holes are formed in the center of galaxies. The Milky Way—home of Earth and the solar system—has a disk of around 100 billion stars swirling around a central bulge. Gas and stars in this bulge appear to fall into a black hole, several millions of times more massive than the Sun.

Primordial black holes may have been formed during the big bang—the enormous explosion that created the universe billions of years ago. Not all the mass in the universe is accounted for, and some scientists think that this missing mass may have ended up trapped inside primordial black holes.

Looking for black holes

Unlike stars, black holes do not emit light, and they cannot be seen directly. Astronomers can still detect black holes, however, by observing their effect on nearby matter such as gas clouds and stars.

Scientists think they have found stellar-mass black holes in binary star systems, where a black hole and star orbit (revolve around) each other. The first suspect is an astronomical object called Cygnus X-1. This invisible X-ray source orbits a star in the constellation Cygnus (the Swan), more than 10,000 light-years away. Cygnus X-1 seems far too dense to be anything other than a black hole. The X-rays would be released as the huge gravitational forces of Cygnus X-1 suck up the gases from the companion star.

How black is a black hole?

In 1974, British physicist Stephen Hawking (1942–) stunned other scientists by showing that black holes emit very weak radiation, called Hawking radiation, even though it is impossible for anything to escape from them. According to quantum theory, empty space is actually a seething mass of pairs of particles. Near the event horizon of a black hole, one member of a pair can be sucked in while

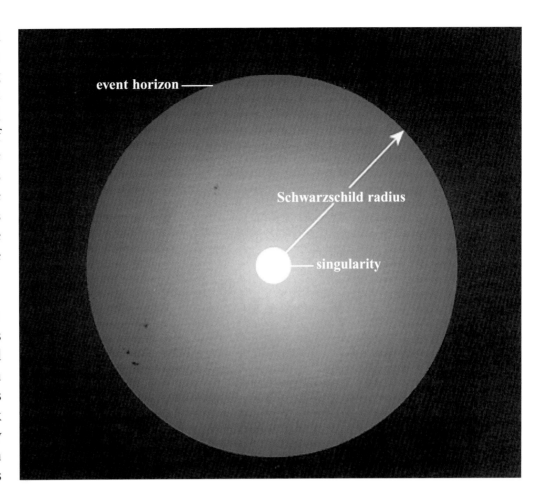

event horizon

Schwarzschild radius

singularity

▲ A black hole may form when a star implodes and shrinks. When the radius of this shrinking star reaches a critical distance—the Schwarzschild radius—the light it emits cannot escape. At this point, the star's surface defines a spherical boundary in space known as the event horizon. Eventually, the star will shrink to a point of infinite density, called a singularity.

the other is shot into space. Hawking concluded that some black holes will evaporate and disappear over billions and billions of years.

White holes and wormholes

Scientists think that there might also be objects in space called white holes—the opposite of black holes. Everything escapes from a white hole, but nothing gets in. Some people think it is possible to connect black and white holes by wormholes to travel to distant galaxies or even to other universes.

See also: ASTRONOMY • GRAVITY • STAR

Blast furnace

For hundreds of years, the blast furnace has provided the main means of iron production. In the furnace, iron ore rock is heated by burning coke (a by product of coal) in hot air. The heat causes chemical reactions to take place, and the ore produces liquid iron.

▲ *The Corus blast furnace at Port Talbot in South Wales operates continuously, producing more than 1½ million tons (1.3 million tonnes) of iron every year.*

The blast furnace gets its name from the blast of hot air that it uses to heat metal ore. Metal ore is rock that contains a high proportion of a particular metal. Most metals are found as ores. In order to be used, these metals must be extracted from the mixed, impure state in which they are found in the ore. To do this, some metal ores can be melted and, using certain chemical processes, the pure metal extracted as a liquid (smelting). Some of the metals produced in this way include copper, tin, and, most significantly, iron. Iron is the most widely used of all metals, with approximately 594 million tons (540 million tonnes) produced annually. Iron is either used pure, usually being cast, or used with carbon to make an alloy called steel. Iron and steel are used in an enormous variety of household and industrial applications.

The chemical process

The type of chemical reaction that converts iron ore into iron is an oxidation and reduction (redox) reaction. Iron ore consists mainly of iron oxide, a combination of iron and oxygen. The reduction of iron oxide removes the oxygen from it, so that pure iron is formed.

In the modern blast furnace, coke is burned in hot air. Coke is coal that has been roasted to get rid of bitumen, sulfur, and other impurities to leave mostly just the carbon. Iron ore is added to the furnace, along with limestone, which combines with some of the impurities in the ore and coke in secondary reactions to help purify the iron. The burning carbon combines with oxygen from the air to form the gas carbon monoxide. The reaction is represented by the following equation:

$$2C + O_2 \rightarrow 2CO$$
carbon + oxygen → carbon monoxide

The carbon monoxide given off by the burning coke then combines with the oxygen (oxidizes) in the heated iron oxide to form carbon dioxide gas. The iron oxide, having given up its oxygen (reduced), becomes pure iron. The equation representing this chemical reaction is as follows:

$$Fe_2O_3 + 3CO \rightarrow 2Fe + 3CO_2$$
iron ore + carbon monoxide → iron + carbon dioxide

These equations describe the main reactions that take place in the blast furnace. However, the process is actually more complicated. Iron ore contains other compounds apart from iron oxide, and both carbon from the coke and carbon monoxide play further parts in the process. Also, the iron produced is not pure. It contains about four percent carbon. In fact, without this carbon content, the blast furnace process would not work. For pure iron melts at 2300°F (1530°C), which is too high a temperature for practical commercial operation. However, the presence of carbon in the iron reduces the melting point to about 2100°F (1150°C). As the furnace operates above this temperature, the iron is produced in liquid form, so it can be collected and run off (tapped) as a liquid.

HISTORY OF THE BLAST FURNACE

The first smelting furnaces were invented by the Chinese. By at least the fourth century CE, they had developed furnaces to obtain iron from iron ore. This was 1,200 years before the first smelting furnace appeared in Europe. The Chinese had access to large amounts of clay, the key ingredient in making furnaces. The Chinese also figured out that by adding a substance they called black earth (thought to be coal) they could lower the melting point of iron. This made the process quicker and more efficient. These early forges were not hot enough to produce molten iron for casting. The iron produced was called "sponge iron," a soft mass of iron which, once some of the waste rock had melted out, was left full of holes. This early, impure iron was then broken into smaller pieces and hammered, or wrought, to beat out the remaining waste. It was then shaped into blooms, or bars. These were later forged into tools or weapons.

The origins of the blast furnace are in the Middle Ages. Furnaces had always had bellows to fan their fires. Air was blown into nozzles, called tuyeres, in the sides of the furnace. But early bellows were small, hand operated devices. By 1400 CE, waterwheels were being used for iron making. These waterwheels operated much larger bellows, to provide constant and powerful blasts of air. The extra oxygen from this air blasting significantly increased the heat in the furnace. The extra heat meant that molten iron could be produced. This was both purer than iron made before, and easier to work with. Liquid iron could simply be run off and set as blocks, or "pigs," of cast iron without the need for hammering first. Waterwheels were also used to power mechanical hammers in forges and stamping mills, and crushing machines used to crush iron ore.

◀ *A 20-ton (18.1-tonne) shovel dumps iron ore at the Algoma steel mill in Ontario, Canada. The 200-foot- (61-meter-) long crane is used to unload ore ships and load ore rail cars for a blast furnace.*

The Iron revolution

Additional major improvements to furnaces were made in the 1700s and 1800s. Warfare in Europe had created increasing demand for iron, and wood for charcoal was becoming scarce. Coal always left impurities, such as sulfur and phosphorus, which made iron brittle. In 1709, Englishman Abraham Darby (1678–1717) became the first person to use coke as a heat source instead of charcoal. This advanced the mass production of brass and iron goods. The quality of Abraham Darby's iron made it possible for him to manufacture thin castings that could compete successfully with brass in many manufacturing applications.

In 1766, Englishman John Wilkinson (1708–1728) introduced the use of steam power to force the air into the furnace. He built a "blowing engine" based on a Watt steam engine. This further increased the heat in the furnace to produce even better quality iron more efficiently.

In 1828, Scotsman James Neilson (1792–1865) developed the technique of preheating the air used in the blast. Hotter, less dense air aided the efficiency and reliability of the burning process.

These advances in iron making made by Darby, Wilkinson, and Neilson proved to be of great importance to the Industrial Revolution, and to the strength and success of the British Empire.

MODERN BLAST FURNACES

The techniques used in modern blast furnaces are essentially the same as those developed by the end of the Industrial Revolution, although modern technology has improved upon them. Greater knowledge of chemical processes has also meant that even better quality metals can be produced.

DID YOU KNOW?

Nearly all the world's iron is produced in blast furnaces. The largest blast furnaces can produce as much as 13,000 tons (11,800 tonnes) of iron per day and run nonstop for many years.

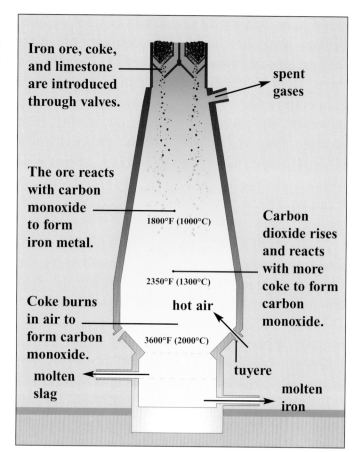

Iron ore, coke, and limestone are introduced through valves.

spent gases

The ore reacts with carbon monoxide to form iron metal.

1800°F (1000°C)

Carbon dioxide rises and reacts with more coke to form carbon monoxide.

2350°F (1300°C)

Coke burns in air to form carbon monoxide.

hot air

3600°F (2000°C)

tuyere

molten slag

molten iron

▲ This diagram of a blast furnace shows how liquid iron is produced from iron ore. As the coke burns and the ore and limestone melt, liquid iron forms at the bottom of the furnace, from where it can be run off.

Furnace operation

In a modern blast furnace, the solid material, or burden, is fed into the top. The burden for making iron consists of iron ore, coke, and limestone.

Air is preheated to about 1800°F (1000°C) by large gas burners and blown through the tuyeres (vents) near the bottom of the furnace. As the hot air passes up through the burden in the furnace, it ignites the coke and thus starts the first part of the chemical process. Carbon monoxide is formed, and this reduces the iron ore to iron. As the coke burns hotter, the temperature in the furnace continues to rise, so that the iron produced is liquid. Because it is most dense, the liquid iron gradually collects at the bottom of the furnace.

The limestone in the furnace fluxes, or purifies, the iron. It helps some of the impurities in the ore and coke to fuse, or melt. Impurities are present

Iron is the major component of steel. A large proportion of the iron used comes from recycled scrap. Here, scrap iron is being melted and refined in a foundry ready to be used for steel production.

DID YOU KNOW?

Iron is the major component of steel. To make steel, specially treated iron is combined with other chemical elements. Carbon steels are made by adding carbon and manganese. Alloy steels are made by further adding nickel, chromium, or molybdenum.

because iron ore is not entirely pure iron oxide, and coke is not pure carbon. The impurities combine with the limestone to form a waste material called slag. This floats on the molten iron. The slag and iron can, therefore, be drawn off separately in their molten states. The whole production process is usually continuous. Once started, modern blast furnaces can operate nonstop for over ten years.

Other methods of making iron are in use, but the blast furnace process seems likely to remain the main method of large-scale iron production.

Structure and siting

Modern blast furnaces are large, tower-like buildings, often more than 100 feet (30 meters) high. The main vessel of the furnace is 25 feet (8 meters) in diameter, with a lining of heat-resistant material more than 3 feet (1 meter) thick. This lining is designed to withstand the very high temperatures inside the furnace. Above the furnace are gas pipes and equipment for loading the furnace. The hearth, or base, of the furnace measures up to about 45 feet (14 meters).

Blast furnaces used to be built close to supplies of iron ore, limestone, and coal suitable for making into coke. But now the raw materials often have to be brought in from other countries. The furnaces are mostly sited near ports or major waterways, which avoids the high cost of having to transport the raw materials over land. The overall cost of producing the iron is, therefore, reduced.

See also: IRON AND STEEL • OXIDATION AND REDUCTION

Bohr, Niels

Danish physicist Niels Bohr ranks alongside Albert Einstein as one of the greatest scientists of the twentieth century. Bohr made many important contributions to science, but one of his greatest achievements came in 1922 when he was awarded the Nobel Prize for physics in recognition of his work on atomic structure.

Niels Bohr was born in Copenhagen, Denmark, on October 7, 1885. Bohr came from a well-educated and prosperous family. His father, Christian, was a professor of physiology at Copenhagen University. His mother, Ellen, came from a wealthy Jewish family with links in banking, education, and politics. The young Bohr showed an interest and talent for science, and his parents did all they could to encourage him.

DID YOU KNOW?

Niels Bohr's brother, Harald, was a gifted soccer player. Harald helped the Danish national team win a silver medal in the 1908 Olympics in London.

Early education

Bohr started his formal education at Gammelholm Grammar School. In 1903, he took a place at Copenhagen University. As a university student, Bohr came under the influence of the highly respected physicist Christian Christiansen. Bohr also decided to specialize in physics.

In 1908, the Royal Danish Academy of Sciences and Letters announced they were to award a prize for the solution of any scientific problem. Bohr took up the challenge and conducted his experiments in his father's laboratory. Bohr won

▲ *Niels Bohr made a huge contribution to science by developing a theory of atomic structure. Later in his life, Bohr was a passionate advocate for the control of nuclear weapons, which he had helped to create.*

the prize for his accurate method of calculating the surface tension of water. The investigation became Bohr's first published scientific paper when it appeared in *Transactions of the Royal Society* (1908).

A year after his first paper was published, Bohr was awarded a master's degree in physics. In 1911, Bohr left Copenhagen University with a doctorate.

Moving abroad

In the fall of 1911, Bohr went to England to work with British physicist J. J. Thomson (1856–1940) at the Cavendish Laboratory, Cambridge University. Bohr wanted to continue developing the theory of electrons that he had worked on at Copenhagen,

◀ *This photograph shows the interior of the European Organization for Nuclear Research (CERN) at Geneva, Switzerland. Bohr was instrumental in creating this important research center.*

A new position

In 1916, Bohr took up a position as professor of physics at Copenhagen University. In 1920, an Institute of Theoretical Physics was established, and Bohr remained its director until his death in 1962. The Institute hosted many important physicists, and it became a center for discussion of modern theories of quantum and wave mechanics.

but Thomson did not show much interest in his ideas. A year later, Bohr moved to Manchester University to join the laboratory of New Zealand–born British physicist Ernest Rutherford (1871–1937). Rutherford's group was studying the structure of the atom.

During his four years at Manchester University, Bohr developed his theory of atomic structure. During his time as a student at Copenhagen University, Bohr had read about the work of German physicist Max Planck (1858–1947). In 1900, Planck developed an idea called quantum theory, which stated that energy consists of indivisible units that he called quanta. Planck's discovery revolutionized physics in the early twentieth century. Many scientists were critical of Planck's work, but Bohr realized that quantum theory could explain some of the problems with Rutherford's model. Rutherford proposed that the dense nucleus at the center of every atom was surrounded by a cloud of tiny particles called electrons. Using quantum theory, Bohr realized that the electrons did not form a cloud but remained at fixed distances from the nucleus. Further, Bohr stated that electrons at each fixed distance had a set energy level. In 1922, Bohr was awarded the Nobel Prize for physics in recognition of his work on atomic structure.

Later life

In the 1930s, Bohr developed important ideas about the nucleus of an atom. He compared a nucleus to a drop of liquid. When bombarded with particles, the drop could absorb some particles and give off others. Very large drops might even be split in two. His ideas led to an understanding of nuclear fission (splitting a nucleus).

A prize for peace

During World War II (1939–1945), Bohr was forced to flee from Denmark to escape arrest for his anti-Nazi views. Bohr first took his family to Sweden, then on to Britain, and finally to the United States.

During his time in the United States, Bohr helped to develop the atom bomb. However, Bohr expressed his concern at the vast destructive power this new weapon would have. Later, he argued for the free flow of people and ideas between all the countries of the world. He felt that such openness would encourage the peaceful use of atomic energy. In 1955, Bohr organized the first Atoms for Peace world conference, held in Geneva, Switzerland. In 1957, he was honored with the first U.S. Atoms for Peace Award, presented by the Ford Foundation.

See also: ATOM AND MOLECULE • PARTICLE PHYSICS

Bomb and shell

Bombs and shells are explosive devices used mainly in warfare. Bombs may be thrown, dropped from aircraft, or placed in position. Most explode when they hit their target, but some bombs can be set to detonate at another time or can be detonated by remote control. Shells are projectiles fired from artillery such as guns. Some shells detonate on impact. Others explode in the air above a target, causing widespread damage.

▲ *A United States Air Force B-1B Lancer drops cluster bombs at a target during the conflict in Afghanistan in 2002. Human rights organizations are concerned about the use of cluster bombs. Some bombs do not explode on impact, and they become dangerous, unexploded "duds." At least 4,000 civilians were killed or injured by cluster bomb duds following the 1991 Gulf War.*

Bombs and shells have a relatively short history in warfare. Chinese scientists developed gunpowder—the first explosive material—around 1000 CE. It took another two hundred years for gunpowder to reach Europe, after which explosive shells and bombs started to appear. In the modern technological age, these weapons are now more sophisticated than ever.

Early shells

Shells are projectiles fired from artillery with a propellant charge. The first shells were used in the fifteenth century. They were simple containers for metal or stone shot, which was dispersed when the container burst after being fired from a gun. Explosive shells came into use in the sixteenth century. These were hollow cast-iron balls filled with gunpowder. They had crude fuses and would explode shortly before or just after hitting the target. These explosive shells were called bombs. Although this is where the word originates, *bomb* now means ammunition that is not fired from a gun.

Early shells were fired from muzzle-loading cannons called mortars. Mortars fire shells at low velocity and high trajectories over short ranges. The shot or bomb drops onto the target from above. In the nineteenth century, shells were developed for direct-fire artillery—large guns and cannons that fire directly at targets at high velocity and at low trajectories. This type of artillery is more powerful than mortars. It also has a longer range. Another major development was shrapnel—a type of antipersonnel projectile named after its inventor Henry Shrapnel (1761–1842), a British artillery officer. Shrapnel shells contained small shot, usually made of lead, along with an explosive charge to scatter the shot and fragments of the shell casing. A time fuse set off the explosive charge near the end of the shell's flight directly above the enemy troops. The resulting hail of high-velocity debris was often lethal. Shrapnel caused the majority of artillery-inflicted wounds during World War I (1914–1918). During World War II (1939–1945), military experts found that a high-explosive charge fragmented the shell's iron casing more effectively. As a result, the use of shrapnel balls became unnecessary. The term *shrapnel* continued to be used to describe the shell-casing fragments.

Modern shells

Modern high-explosive artillery shells consist of a shell casing, a propelling charge, and a bursting charge. The propelling charge is ignited by a primer at the base of the shell. The bursting charge is

ignited by a fuse in the nose. There are many different kinds of modern artillery shells. Armor-piercing shells can blast through thick steel armor. They have a pointed nose made of hardened steel that penetrates the armor, allowing the bursting charge to detonate inside the target. HEP (high-explosive plastic) antitank shells have thin metal casings filled with plastic explosives. When an HEP shell hits a tank, the casing splits open. The plastic explosive sticks to the target before it explodes, inflicting more serious damage to the tank.

Most shells are "dumb," which means they do not have a guiding mechanism. Once they leave the gun, the gunner has no control over them. Some modern shells are "smart," or guided. Smart shells are much more accurate. The shells are steered by wings and fins that fold out after the shell has been fired. One of the most common smart shells is the U.S. military's Copperhead guided shell (see the illustration on page 208). The target is identified with a laser marker, which is fired at the target previously or positioned by troops. A laser detector in the shell's nose identifies the target. The shell then pinpoints the target before detonating.

▲ A Lancaster bomber of Royal Air Force Bomber Command drops bombs on an oil refinery at Bremen, Germany, on March 21, 1945. During World War II (1939–1945), Allied forces dropped about 2 million tons (1.8 million tonnes) of bombs on German targets.

Bombs

Unlike shells, bombs do not have a propellant charge. Instead they are dropped from aircraft and fall to the target by gravity, or they are thrown or positioned by hand. Most bombs dropped from aircraft have four main parts: a body packed with explosive or some other contents; a fin assembly to stabilize the bomb in flight; a fuse; and a device to arm (activate) the bomb at the moment of release.

The body (casing) of the bomb usually has a smooth, streamlined shape and a pointed nose. A simple tail-fin assembly ensures a smooth flight. The design of the bomb casing depends on the way it is required to burst. Bombs used against people are designed to shatter into shrapnel to cause as much injury as possible. Armor-piercing bombs have a pointed, high-strength case to penetrate armor. There are two main types of fuses. An impact fuse detonates a bomb when it strikes its

▶ *United States Air Force ground crew load a B-52H Stratofortress with MK 82 bombs in preparation for a bombing mission. MK 82 bombs are used in bombing operations where maximum blast and explosive effects are desired.*

target. A time fuse acts after a timed delay. The fuses must have safety devices to make sure the bombs do not go off accidentally during handling. Usually, a wire attached to the fuses arms the bombs as they are released from the aircraft.

Development of bombs

Balloons carried the first aerial bombs, but the development of the airplane made bombing much more effective. Early bombs, as used at the beginning of World War I, were simple artillery shells with fins at one end and an impact fuse at the other. They were light, and pilots threw them out of the airplane. Bombing tactics improved steadily, and it soon became possible to deliver heavy bombs to distant targets. This was done using airships and, later, modified fighter-bomber aircraft.

Bombing played a much greater role in World War II. Larger planes could carry bigger bombs. Mechanical and radio targeting devices helped pilots or bombers target bombs more accurately. Different kinds of bombs also began to be developed, including incendiary (fire) bombs and poisonous chemical bombs. During the Vietnam War (1954–1975), guidance systems controlled by laser, electro-optics, and infrared were used. Modern bombs are developing faster than ever, alongside other emerging technologies.

Types of bombs

A wide variety of bombs is available to use against many targets. Armor-piercing bombs are designed to penetrate concrete-reinforced structures and armor plate. Depth charges are designed for

GUIDANCE SECTION	WARHEAD SECTION	CONTROL SECTION

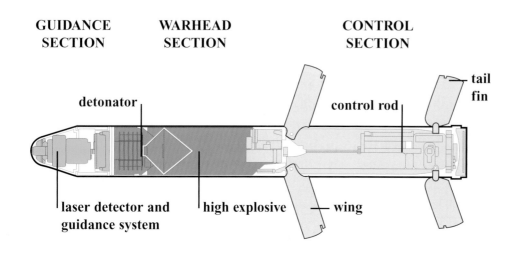

detonator

laser detector and guidance system

high explosive

wing

control rod

tail fin

◀ *The Cannon-Launched Guided Projectile, or Copperhead, developed by the U.S. military, was the first practical guided shell. The shell homes in on reflections from a laser marker fired at the target. The data is then fed into a guidance system, which adjusts the wings and fins to steer the shell to impact. The high explosive warhead detonates on impact.*

underwater warfare. A pressure-operated fuse sets off the charge when the bomb reaches the set depth. Chemical bombs can contain smoke or deadly poisonous gases. Incendiary bombs use flammable oily mixtures, such as napalm, to destroy ground targets.

Atomic bombs and hydrogen bombs release enormous amounts of energy from nuclear reactions. Both types are so devastating that the heat from the flash ignites buildings and destroys every living creature over a large area. The nuclear bomb dropped on Hiroshima, Japan, by the United States during World War II killed as many as 80,000 people. The shock from the blast brought trees and buildings crashing to the ground, and harmful radioactive dust contaminated a wide area. Because of their enormous power, nuclear weapons are controlled by international treaties.

▲ *A house at "Survival City" in Nevada is torn apart by nuclear test blast "Annie" on March 17, 1953. This blast was the second of a series of military tests known as Operation Upshot-Knothole.*

Modern smart bombs use global positioning systems (GPS) to pinpoint the target. A GPS sensor carrying preprogrammed coordinates directs the bomb. Once released over the target, the bomb finds its mark to within a few feet. Some smart bombs disable enemy infrastructure without destroying it. Graphite bombs explode over power plants, showering the area with conductive carbon filaments that short out the power lines. Electromagnetic bombs release a burst of electromagnetic energy, disabling computer systems.

See also: EXPLOSIVE • GUN • NUCLEAR WEAPON

Botany

Botany is the scientific study of plants. It has made great advances in the last few years. Using genetic engineering, botanists can now give one plant species the features of another. They have also discovered that plants behave in ways never before realized.

Using genetic engineering, botanists (plant scientists) can now alter a plant's characteristics very precisely. For example, genetically engineered corn now resists its worst pest—the European corn borer. Botanists have added a gene that makes the plant produce an insecticide. The insecticide poisons only the European corn borer but is harmless to other creatures, including humans.

Another example is a new gene that has been implanted into wheat. The gene makes the wheat resistant to a specific herbicide. This allows a farmer to spray the herbicide on a field to kill weeds without harming the wheat.

People have benefited from genetic engineering in many ways, but developments have not come without their drawbacks. In 1991, *Flavr Savr* tomatoes were hailed as the first fresh genetically modified (GM) food. Unlike ordinary tomatoes, the *Flavr Savr* variety was designed to stay riper for longer. *Flavr Savr* tomatoes were also easier to transport, because they did not bruise or perish as easily as ordinary tomatoes. However, many people were concerned about the possible negative health effects associated with GM food, and the sale of *Flavr Savr* tomatoes was rapidly withdrawn.

Plants behaving like animals

Botanists have discovered that plants behave much more like animals than had been imagined. In particular, it appears that plants have a sense of touch and may even have a simple way of communicating with each other.

▼ *A botanist studies the leaf of a tomato plant to see how it functions in cool night temperatures. Light guides and hoses lead to instruments that measure the photosynthetic activity of the leaf.*

Some plants, such as the Venus's-flytrap, have a sense of touch that triggers their movements. This was once thought to be unusual, but it now seems that all plants have a sense of touch. Stroking a plant stem for a few seconds a day is enough to stunt its growth and widen its stem. In nature this reaction allows plants that are buffeted by the wind to grow tougher stems that will not snap.

Stroking plants also stimulates their metabolism and chlorophyll production. It also makes the plants close pores called stomata. This limits water loss. Horticulturalists (people who grow garden crops, such as fruits, commercially) are now looking to see how they can make use of these effects.

How does plant touch work?

In 1989, special touch sensors were discovered in plant cell membranes. When the cells are stretched, the sensors open and let ions through, changing the voltage across the membrane. Exactly the same thing happens in animal cells, telling touch-sensitive nerves when to send signals to the brain.

Plants have no nerves. It is not clear whether plants also use electric signals when they detect touch, but botanists are learning about many chemical reactions triggered by the touch sensors. In 1990, a discovery was made by chance. Scientists noticed that touching or simply spraying a plant with water triggered activity by certain genes.

◀ *Genetically modified barley in California now carries a gene that helps the plants resist attack by barley yellow dwarf virus (BYDV), which is spread by grain aphids.*

▲ *Oak trees produce tannins to ward off attack by harmful insects. The trees secrete the tannins in response to chemical messengers sent by neigboring plants, such as sagebrush.*

Research revealed that these genes make a protein involved in the control of calcium ions. These ions are a vital signal for redirecting plant growth.

In 1992, researchers at Edinburgh University, Scotland, turned this chemistry into a practical tool. They inserted a gene into potato plants to make the plant cells glow whenever they released calcium under stress. Even touching the plant made the cells glow sky blue. Researchers hope that farmers will use this gene, along with light meters, to monitor the health of crops such as potatoes.

Plant talk

Recent research has revealed a chemical language between plants. Interest in plant communication began when oak trees that were being attacked by caterpillars were found to respond by making tannins. These chemicals taste bitter to insects. Nearby oak trees that had not been attacked also started making tannins. Somehow the infested trees had warned their neighbors. Exactly how this

worked remained a mystery until 1990, when a scent signal was discovered in sagebrush. When a sagebrush is attacked by insects, it produces insect-fighting proteins. It also emits a scent as a chemical message to tell neighboring plants to do the same.

Airborne signals are also used by plants to recruit helpful insects. In 1990, botanists discovered a scent released by corn plants infested by caterpillars. The scent attracted parasitic wasps to the plants and appeared to act like a distress message. The wasps laid their eggs inside the caterpillars, and the hatching wasp larvae (young) killed the caterpillars.

Desert plants have also been found to communicate. When roots from different plant species grow near each other, they often avoid one another. The plants give off warning signals by secreting chemical messages into the soil.

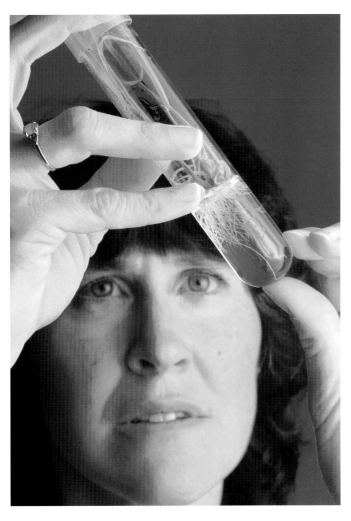

▲ *A geneticist looks at roots on genetically engineered wheat plants. It is hoped that they may carry new genes for resistance to the pest fungus* **Fusarium.**

Aspirin

It has long been known that plants make aspirin. In fact the name *aspirin* comes from the Latin name for the plant meadowsweet (*Spiraea*). But until recently, no one could figure out why plants contain aspirin. The answer came from the voodoo lily, which is a tropical plant with an unusual bloom. On the outside, it looks like a purple poker wrapped up in a green sheath, nipped at the bottom into a small chamber. When the bloom becomes fertile, the poker suddenly heats up and emits a rotten smell. This is perfume to flies, which flock to the poker and crawl down the sheath and pollinate the hidden flowers. The signal that triggers the poker to heat up turned out to be salicylic acid, which is a chemical cousin of aspirin.

This discovery led scientists to investigate how salicylic acid affected other plants. They found that plants attacked by diseases make salicylic acid to fight the infection. It may also allow them to withstand cold weather. Agricultural companies are now looking at ways to apply the chemical to crops or to breed plants with high levels of salicylic acid.

Plant hormones

Botanists have discovered many new plant hormones. These chemicals circulate through the plant, carrying messages from cell to cell, just like the hormones in animals. In fact, plant hormones are closely related to animal hormones.

Chemicals called prostaglandins have been found in bean seedlings. In animals, prostaglandins trigger pain in wounds. Their purpose in plants is not yet clear. Serotonin, norepinephrine, and acetylcholine, which carry messages between animal nerve cells, occur in many plants. Acetylcholine seems to be involved in plant biorhythms, telling the time by recording the hours of daylight. Animals also use acetylcholine in this way, as well as for passing nerve messages.

Estrogens and testosterones regulate sexual behavior in animals. In plants, they help flowering and stimulate mating in fungi. One of the most common plant hormones, gibberellic acid, is another close relation to the animal sex hormones. Gibberellic acid regulates plant growth.

Scientists believe that both plants and animals evolved from tiny single-celled creatures. These creatures also contain hormones. Baker's yeast cells contain estrogen. A pear-shaped protist called *Chlamydomonas* steers itself along using a propeller guided by rhodopsin, the light-sensitive pigment in mammalian eyes. It seems animals and plants inherited the same chemical building blocks. Animals went on to develop a nervous and muscle system, while plants formed a primitive sensory system without having nerves.

See also: BIOLOGY • GENETIC ENGINEERING • PLANT KINGDOM

Brain

The brain is a mass of nerve cells that controls almost everything that goes on inside the body. Nerve cells carry electrical signals to and from the brain and around the body. The human brain is also home to the mind, which is used to think, dream, and feel emotions.

The brain is the control center of the human body. It processes the information that is supplied to it and then sends instructions around the body through a complex network called the nervous system. The brain works like a computer, but it can do many more tasks at once than even the most powerful computer. The human brain is also home to the mind. The mind is not a physical organ. It is probably the result of several parts of the brain working together. The mind thinks and imagine things, and it is the source of a person's emotions and personality. Most animal brains are simple control devices, but some animals, such as chimpanzees, may have intelligent minds similar to humans. They govern every single body function, from the beating of the heart to the movements of the digestive system.

Inside the brain

The brain is the heart of the nervous system—a complex network of thin nerve fibers extending throughout the body. The central nervous system (CNS) connects all the nerve fibers in the body. It

▼ *The human brain is a mass of more than 100 billion nerve cells, or neurons.*

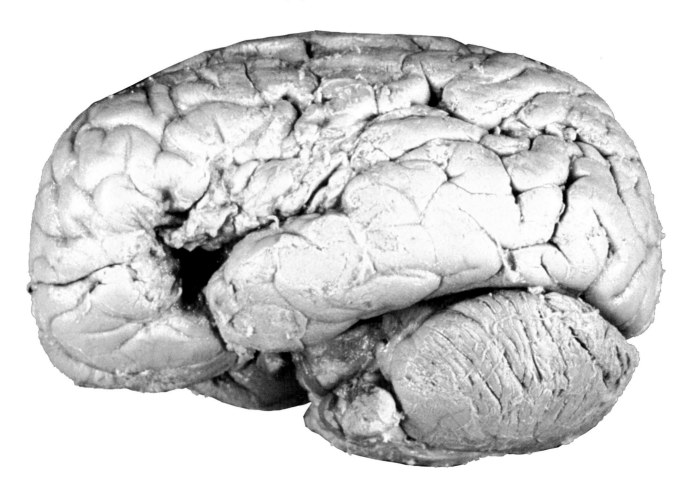

comprises the brain and the spinal cord. The spinal cord is a thick bundle of nerves that runs from the base of the brain down the back. This delicate column of nerve tissue is protected by the spine, or backbone. Most nerve signals traveling between the body and the brain move along the spinal cord.

The brain itself is encased in a tough, protective layer of bone called the skull. The surface of the brain is also protected by three membranes called meninges. (Meningitis is the name given to the disease that affects these membranes.) A clear liquid, called cerebrospinal fluid, is held between two of the three membranes. This fluid protects the soft brain as it moves around inside the skull.

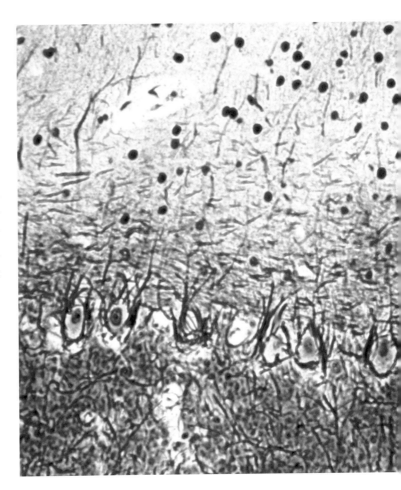

▶ *These large neurons are called Purkinje cells, named for Czech scientist Jan Purkinje (1787–1869) who discovered them 150 years ago. Like other neurons, Purkinje cells have long extensions, called axons, that carry signals around the brain.*

▼ *An astrocyte, a star-shaped glial cell, is wrapped around a blood vessel inside the brain. Astrocytes prevent harmful substances from leaking out of the blood into the fluid that bathes the brain's cells.*

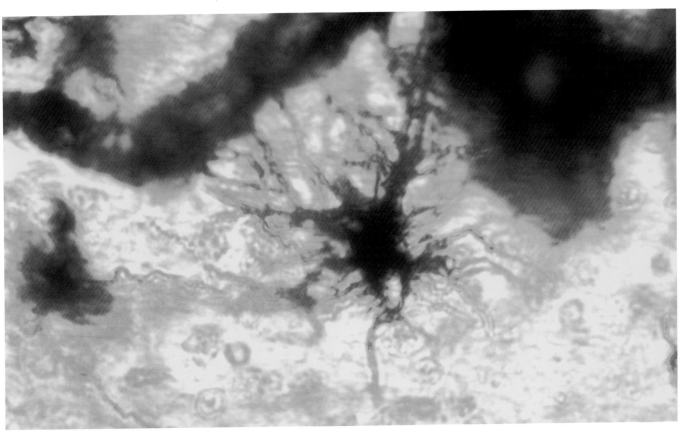

The brain itself consists of two types of cells. Neurons produce electric pulses that make up the nerve signals. Neurons have long, thin extensions that branch out toward other cells. The pulses travel along these branches, called axons. The other cells in the brain are called glia. The name *glia* comes from the Greek word for "glue." Glial cells surround the neurons and perform a number of roles. Some provide a supportive framework for the neurons and clean up any dead neurons by engulfing and then digesting them. Another glial cell will then grow into a new neuron. Other glial cells produce a fatty substance called myelin, which is used to coat the axons of some neurons. The coating makes nerve signals travel faster. Myelin is a white substance, and areas of the brain that contain a lot of myelin-coated cells are called white matter. Areas that are consist of neurons that do not have myelin coats are called gray matter.

▶ **Doctors can look at the structure of the brain with an MRI scanner. This device uses magnets and radio waves to construct a still image of the living brain.**

▼ **PET-scanning is used to study how the brain is working. It produces moving colored images that represent the activity in different parts of the brain.**

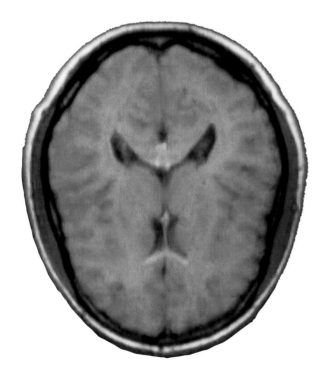

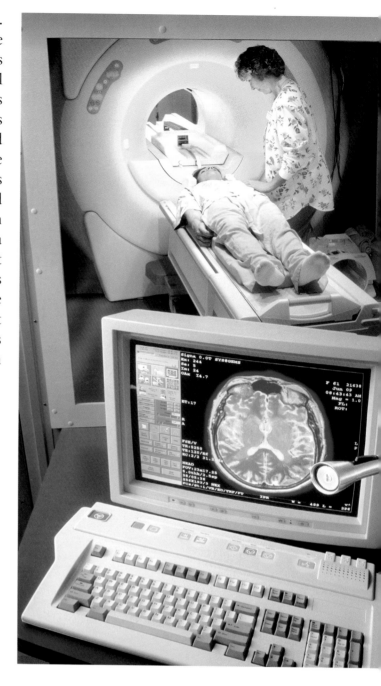

The structure of the brain

The human brain is divided into three main sections: the brain stem, the cerebellum, and the cerebrum. These sections are joined together, but they each perform a specific set of roles. The brain stem, which is the top of the spinal cord, is the central part of the brain from which the other two parts extend. The lower part of the brain stem is called the medulla oblongata. This area controls the most essential body functions, such as breathing and heartbeat. Above the medulla is the pons. *Pons*

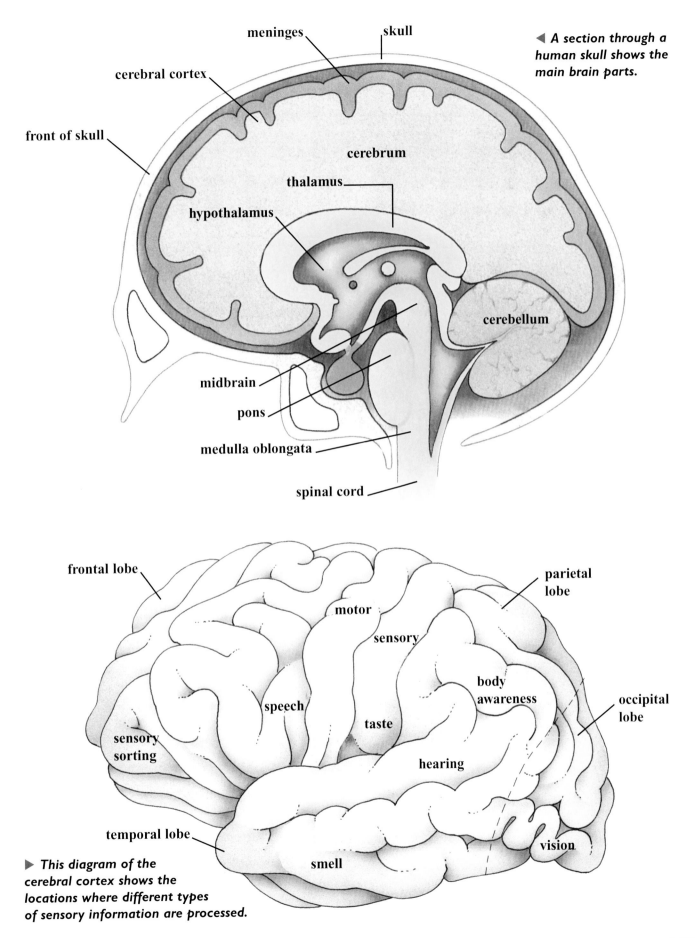

meninges

skull

◀ *A section through a human skull shows the main brain parts.*

cerebral cortex

cerebrum

front of skull

thalamus

hypothalamus

cerebellum

midbrain

pons

medulla oblongata

spinal cord

frontal lobe

parietal lobe

motor

sensory

speech

body awareness

occipital lobe

sensory sorting

taste

hearing

temporal lobe

vision

smell

▶ *This diagram of the cerebral cortex shows the locations where different types of sensory information are processed.*

means "bridge" in Latin, and this area is the link between the cerebellum and the cerebrum. The third part of the brain stem is the midbrain. It lies just above the pons and controls other basic body functions and automatic movements, such as the movement of the eyes. At the top of the brain stem is the thalamus, which contains the hypothalamus. The thalamus is the router for information coming into the brain heading for the cerebrum. It organizes where all the signals should be sent. The hypothalamus regulates body temperature, hunger, and other internal sensations, including pain.

The word *cerebellum* means "little brain." This section of the brain is attached to the back of the brainstem and is under the cerebrum. It is responsible for controlling balance, posture, and coordination. Once children learn to walk or ride a bicycle, it is the cerebellum that remembers how the body needs to move. And when they walk or ride again, they can do it without thinking.

Main brain

The cerebrum is the largest part of the human brain. It is divided into two halves, called hemispheres, which are connected by a bundle of nerve fibers at the brain's center. Each hemisphere is divided into four lobes. The outermost area of the cerebrum is called the cerebral cortex. This consists of a dense mass of gray matter. The nerve fibers coming out of the cerebral cortex's neurons make up most of the lobes beneath it.

The cerebrum is the main control center of the brain. Scientists have discovered that each part of the cerebral cortex deals with a certain type of information. For example, information from the body's sense organs is received by an area called the sensory cortex. Each sense, such as sight, hearing, and touch, is processed by one section of this cortex. The cerebrum also controls voluntary muscle movements, including talking.

▶ *Movie star Michael J. Fox suffers from Parkinson's disease, a brain disorder that makes it hard to control muscles. Sufferers often tremble uncontrollably or can make only stiff movements. The disease is caused by a problem in a part of the cerebrum.*

The cerebrum is also the site of the human mind—the part of a person that allows him or her to think, understand his or her surroundings, and imagine new situations and ideas. Scientists differ in opinion as to whether the behavior of animals indicates the presence of a mind in the same sense that humans have minds. Certainly no animal species has demonstrated the kinds of linguistic and abstract reasoning that typify human thought.

The cerebrum makes up 85 percent of the human brain. Other animals have much smaller cerebrums that are no larger than other parts of the brain. Generally, less intelligent animals, such as fish, have small, smooth cerebrums. More intelligent animals, such as apes or humans, have large cerebrums that

have a heavily folded cerebral cortex. The folds increase the surface area of the brain and provide more space to house more neurons.

People are the most intelligent animals on Earth, but the human brain is not the largest in the animal kingdom. The brain of a three-month-old baby, for example, weighs about 1 pound (0.5 kilograms). It stops growing when a person reaches six years old, when it weighs about 3 pounds (1.4 kilograms). The brain of an elephant is slightly bigger than this; a whale's brain is even bigger. However, these animals have much larger bodies than people. When compared to the size of their bodies, human brains are bigger than those of any other animal.

▼ *Some people are terrified of roller-coaster rides. Their brains respond by producing stress hormones such as serotonin and norepinephrine. Other people feel exhilarated. Their brains react by flooding the body with chemicals called endorphins, which produce the feelings of excitement and euphoria.*

Nerve pathways

The brain deals with a huge amount of information all at once. Some of the nerves around the body carry information from the sensory organs, such as the eyes, ears, and nose, to the brain. These nerves are called sensory nerves. The information from sensory nerves is processed by the brain. Some of it may be simple enough to be dealt with by the brain stem, or even the spinal cord. More complex information is directed up into the cerebral cortex, where the mind can decide what to do about it.

Once a decision has been made, the brain produces its own electric signals, which travel out into the body. The signals contain instructions for the body. They may be telling muscles to move or a gland to produce more or less of a hormone. The nerves that carry these instructions are called motor nerves. The brain often instructs the body to move automatically, without the mind needing to think about it. When a person picks up a hot object,

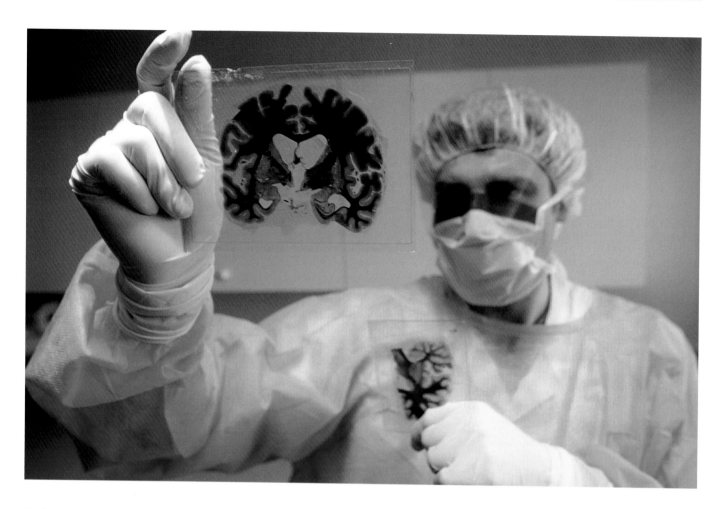

▲ *A scientist studies thin slices of a human brain. This brain belonged to a person who died from Creutzfeldt-Jakob disease (CJD). This disease turns the brain tissue into a spongy, porous mass. The mind and body slowly waste away and CJD victims die a slow death.*

for example, his or her hand will automatically drop it. These automatic actions are called reflexes. Most of them are controlled by the spinal cord. However, the cerebrum can override a reflex. For example, it may be too dangerous to drop the hot object. In this case, the brain will command the body to put the object down somewhere safe, even if the hand holding it is being burned.

Memory and learning

As well as controlling the body, the brain also remembers events from the past, which might prove useful in the future. There is no one part of the brain that stores memories. Scientists think that individual memories are stored as neuron circuits. When a person remembers one memory, the electric signal that passes through the circuit causes chemical changes to occur. The chemicals make more neurons join on to the circuit to reinforce the memory. If a memory is not recalled regularly, the circuit becomes weaker, or is disconnected, and eventually disappears. Since the brain cannot find the circuit, the memory is forgotten.

The human brain has three memories. The first, sensory memory, holds very detailed information for a second or two. These memories soon fade unless a person actively thinks about them, keeping them in the mind. This information then passes to the short-term memory, which is used to hold facts such as telephone numbers. These memories fade after about 20 seconds. Long-term memory stores information even after the mind has stopped thinking about it. The brain solves problems by comparing short-term and long-term memories.

See also: NERVOUS SYSTEM

Brake system

To bring a moving machine, vehicle, or wheel to a stop, the driver or operator uses brakes. Nearly all brakes work by two surfaces rubbing together. If a cyclist drags his or her foot on the ground, for example, the foot moving against the ground creates the friction that stops the bicycle.

Brakes are usually of the revolving type, where a block or band is pressed against a revolving drum or disc. However, not all brakes revolve. For example, the emergency brakes on elevators work when blocks are pressed against the steel guides on which the elevator slides up and down.

Drum brakes
In the most common type of drum brake, two brake shoes are pressed against the inside of a drum fixed to the wheel of the vehicle. In some cases, the brakes work mechanically, but hydraulic or compressed-air systems are now much more common. The parking brakes on automobiles are usually mechanical brakes. Engaging the parking brake causes a series of levers and cables to press the shoes against the drum. This locks the wheel.

Brake shoes are covered with a carefully chosen mixture of materials. These brake linings produce a lot of friction to stop the vehicle, but they must not wear out too quickly. The best results are obtained when the brake linings are used in operation with moving parts made from smooth metal.

Disc brakes
Disc brakes consist of revolving discs attached to the vehicle's wheels. When the brake pedal is applied, these discs are gripped tightly between brake pads. Most automobile disc brakes are hydraulically operated. Hydraulic disc brakes can work at higher temperatures than drum brakes. Disc brakes are used on the front axle of most cars. Most aircraft also have hydraulic disc brakes.

Hydraulic brakes
Nearly all automobiles have hydraulic braking systems. These use the pressure of a liquid to force the brake shoes against the brake drums or, in disc brakes, to squeeze the brake pads against the discs

▲ The disc brake is applied during a test on an automobile braking system.

▲ As the brake pedal is held down, the rotating disc heats up and begins to glow.

▲ Finally the disc slows down, but the heat is now so intense that sparks start to fly.

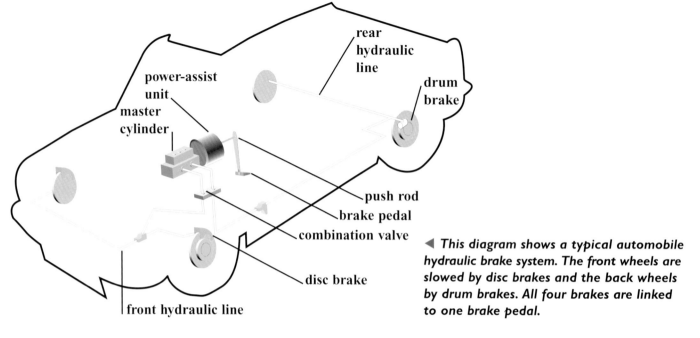

◀ This diagram shows a typical automobile hydraulic brake system. The front wheels are slowed by disc brakes and the back wheels by drum brakes. All four brakes are linked to one brake pedal.

inside the automobile's wheels. The liquid is held in cylinders in each brake. These wheel cylinders are connected by pipes to a master cylinder full of liquid. When the driver presses the brake pedal, a piston is pushed into the master cylinder. This pushes liquid from the master cylinder along pipes to the cylinders in the wheel brakes. This increased pressure pushes the pistons in the wheel cylinders outward, working the brake drums or pads. The vehicle slows down or stops, depending on how hard, and for how long, the brake pedal is pressed.

▼ The three most common brake types are the external block brake, the internal expanding drum brake, and the caliper disc brake. All three types use friction to slow rotating wheels to a stop.

Air brakes

Brakes on buses, trains, and trucks usually operate under the action of compressed air rather than liquid pressure. Railroad brakes are operated by a compressor under the control of the driver or braker. Compressed air from the compressor is fed along the passenger or freight cars by means of a "train pipe," which has to be connected between the cars when they are coupled. When the driver or braker presses on the brake lever, all the brakes on the wheels of the train engage at the same time. Brake blocks rub against the steel tires on the wheels. On some railroad cars, pressure is applied to separate discs on the axles rather than to the train wheels themselves.

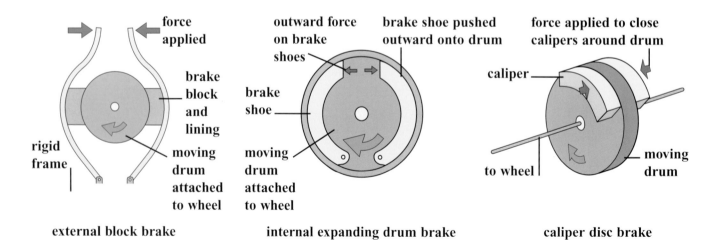

external block brake   internal expanding drum brake   caliper disc brake

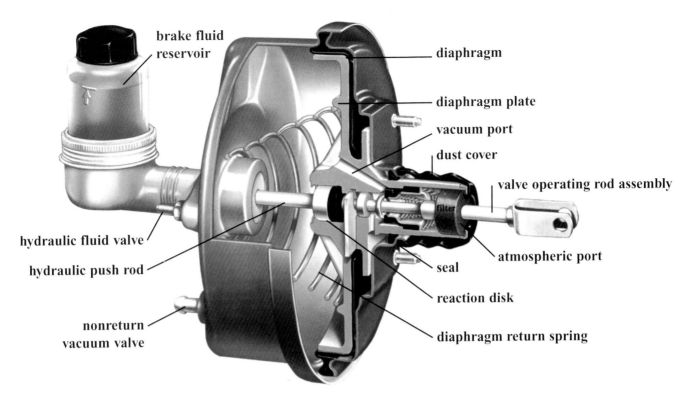

brake fluid
reservoir

diaphragm

diaphragm plate

vacuum port

dust cover

valve operating rod assembly

hydraulic fluid valve

hydraulic push rod

atmospheric port

seal

reaction disk

nonreturn
vacuum valve

diaphragm return spring

▶ *In vacuum servo brakes, a hydraulic push rod runs through an airtight cylinder, which is split into two parts by a metal plate, called the diaphragm plate. A diaphragm makes a seal between the plate and the cylinder walls, and a vacuum is created in the cylinder. When the driver brakes (1), higher-pressure atmospheric air is let into the right-hand side, pushing the plate and hydraulic rod and operating the brake system. A spring returns the plate when the driver releases the brake (2).*

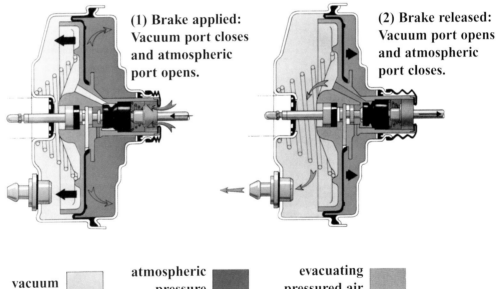

(1) Brake applied:
Vacuum port closes
and atmospheric
port opens.

(2) Brake released:
Vacuum port opens
and atmospheric
port closes.

vacuum

atmospheric
pressure

evacuating
pressured air

The best-known railroad air-brake system is the Westinghouse, which was invented by U.S. businessman George Westinghouse (1846–1914) in 1869. The Westinghouse air-brake system is designed to operate as soon as the pressure in the air pipe drops. If a railroad car broke loose from a train, for example, the train pipe is cut, and the brakes are applied automatically in the breakaway car. Westinghouse's air brakes made train travel much safer than before.

POWER BRAKES

Disc brakes are very efficient, but they must be applied with more force than is needed to work the older drum brakes. So many modern automobile disc brake systems come with power assistance.

Vacuum-assisted brakes

Most power brakes make use of air pressure in one form or another. On private automobiles, this is usually a vacuum servo system. A gasoline engine

▲ *Commercial jets have air brakes built into the wings and disc brakes in the wheels. On landing, the pilot also reverses the direction of thrust from the engines.*

has a partial vacuum of about 10 pounds per square inch (0.65 kilogram per square centimeter) below normal air pressure. This vacuum can be used as a source of power, especially for braking.

A vacuum pipe transfers the partial vacuum from the engine to an airtight chamber, which is divided in two by a movable metal plate. A rod from the brake pedal passes through the chamber and through a hole in the plate. At this point, there is an arrangement that lets the plate push the rod when it moves in one direction. The rod then goes on to operate the brake mechanism.

Valves

A system of valves is worked by the rod, so that one part of the chamber can be connected either to the vacuum or to the outside air. The other side is connected permanently to the vacuum.

When the driver is not braking, the valves are all open to the vacuum, so both halves of the chamber are under a partial vacuum. When the driver brakes, air at normal pressure is let into one chamber. This pushes the plate into the half that still has its vacuum and also helps push the rod along. When the driver releases the brake pedal, the air valve is closed, and the vacuum is again connected to both halves of the chamber. The plate is moved back to its original position by a spring.

Compressed air

In trucks and trains, which usually have compressed air braking systems instead of hydraulics, the engine drives an air compressor pump.

Braking must be progressive. If the driver brakes only gently, then the power system must apply the brakes gently, too. It must always respond accurately to the amount of force on the brake pedal. The braking system must also be designed to be failsafe—if the system breaks down, it must still be possible to stop. In vacuum-assisted brake systems, the driver can brake even if the main system fails, though it will be hard work. With compressed-air brake systems, the truck driver has several separate systems in case one fails.

Airplane brakes

Airplanes are slowed down by air brakes. These are flaps that can be pushed out above and below the wings. They break up the flow of air rushing past the airplane and cause resistance, or drag.

On landing, the wheels' disc brakes are applied, and at the same time the engines are put into reverse thrust. Scoops are pushed into the exhaust stream to turn the stream forward. The effect of this is to try to force the airplane in the opposite direction and thus slow it down. Some extremely fast airplanes are also slowed by parachutes on landing.

See also: AUTOMOBILE • HYDRAULICS

224

Brass

Brass is an alloy—a mixture of the metals copper and zinc. This attractive, hard-wearing alloy has many uses in architecture and engineering and for hardware, musical instruments, and ornamental items. Brass is harder and stronger than copper and does not wear out as easily. It is also cheaper than pure copper.

▲ *Brass can be made in many different ways. One of the most common types of brass is cartridge brass. This is manufactured in long, flat sheets and stored as large rolls. Many products are made using cartridge brass.*

Brass was discovered some time after 1000 BCE by people who lived near the Black Sea in Turkey. They made brass by heating copper with charcoal and powdered zinc ore. By the end of the first century BCE, the Romans were making brass coins. In Europe up to the sixteenth century, brass was used mainly for decorations in churches. After the Industrial Revolution in the eighteenth century it became widely used for manufactured products.

What is brass?

There are many different kinds of brass, but all of them contain copper and zinc. The amount of copper in brass varies from 50 percent to more than 95 percent. Zinc is added in proportions of up to 50 percent. Small amounts of other elements are often added for special purposes. The most common elements added include aluminum, iron, lead, manganese, nickel, or tin.

When brass contains 50 to 70 percent copper, it is a golden yellow color. If the alloy has more than 80 percent copper, it becomes reddish and looks more like pure copper.

Alloys with a lot of copper in them are relatively soft and can be shaped hot or cold. Brass with less than 60 percent copper is not shaped cold because it is too hard and brittle. The more zinc that is added to the mixture, the harder the brass becomes. Small quantities of nickel and tin are often added to make brass harder and more resistant to wear.

Making brass

One of the problems in making brass is the difference in the melting point of the two main ingredients. The melting point of copper is 1990°F (1083°C), but zinc's melting point is only 786°F (419°C). If the metals were heated together all the zinc would boil away before the copper had melted. So the copper has to be heated first until it melts. Then solid zinc is added, and most of it melts quickly in the molten copper. A little extra zinc is added to make up for the small amount that boils away.

Casting the brass

After the zinc and copper have melted and mixed, the brass is ready to be poured into casting molds preshaped to whatever is being made. To prevent the brass from sticking to the molds, the insides are coated with graphite or some oily substance before the molten alloy is poured in.

The brass can also be made into bars called ingots or billets and stored away. These bars will later be melted down to make other brass objects.

Forging

Brass can be forged (hammered) into accurate shapes either hot or cold. Cold forging works best when there is more than 64 percent copper in the brass. Less than this, and the brass is too brittle. The brass is often placed in a die on a heavy anvil. Another part of the die is fixed to the bottom of a giant drop hammer, usually made from a heavy steel block. This block is raised between guides and allowed to drop. The force of the hammer presses the brass into shape between the two dies. Bolts, screws, and door and plumbing fittings are some examples of articles made this way.

Cartridge brass

One of the most common brasses is called cartridge brass. It is made of 70 percent copper and 30 percent zinc. Cartridge brass is produced in large, flat sheets and coiled into rolls. Cartridge cases can be pressed out of flat disks of this brass, even when the metal is cold. Cartridge brass is also used to make plumbing equipment, tubes, and musical instruments.

Nickel silver

Despite its name, nickel silver has no silver in it, but is an alloy of copper, zinc, and nickel. This metal, which is also called German silver, is used to make ornamental "silverware" for the table. Once formed, the metal is plated with silver, and the finished products look like they are made from real silver. The silver can, however, wear off with use.

▲ *Brass is used to make many musical instruments, including trombones and trumpets. Brass instruments have a unique sound, and brass bands are popular throughout the world.*

See also: ALLOY • CASTING • COPPER • MUSICAL INSTRUMENT • ZINC

Bread making

Bread is the most widely eaten food in the world. It contains vitamins and minerals that keep people healthy. Bread is made by a process called baking in which all the ingredients are mixed together to form a dough and then cooked in a hot oven.

Bread is one of the oldest foods in the world. Bread making began when people found they could eat wild grains. It did not take long for people to discover that the grains tasted better if they were cooked in some way. The early bread makers learned to pound the grains between two stones to create a flour, mix this with water to make a paste, spread the paste on flat stones, and bake the paste over an open fire. This was the first type of bread.

This early bread did not rise. It was called unleavened bread and was flat and rather heavy. The next important discovery was made by the ancient Egyptians and Babylonians about 2600 BCE. They started to make yeast bread, which requires a process called fermentation. It was probably discovered accidentally when a piece of old dough was added to a new piece of dough. If the dough is left for a few days, a chemical process takes place inside it, which produces bubbles of carbon dioxide gas (CO_2). This causes the bread to rise (grow larger) and become light and porous. The gas is given off by yeast, a microorganism that is present naturally in flour. But the yeast needs a few days to multiply until there is enough of it to make the bread rise.

▼ *A baker removes some freshly baked bread from an oven. Large, modern bakeries are more like factories, and the bread-making process is highly automated.*

◀ *A Thai woman fills a village millstone with grain before grinding it into fine flour. Communal millstones are common in many poor and remote parts of the world, where bread making is still done by hand.*

▼ *Dough is mixed in a large vat at a commercial bakery. Modern bakeries rely on machines to meet the huge daily demand for bread.*

Cooking bread at home started to decline in the Middle Ages as small bakeries opened in villages and towns across Europe. Large brick ovens were built to bake the bread, and they were heated by wood or coal. Brick ovens are still used by bakers today, but they are now heated by gas or oil.

For hundreds of years, people ate bread made with whole wheat or whole grain flour. White flour is more versatile for baking, but it used to be very expensive to produce. Milling the grain (grinding it using stones) required hours of work. In the 1870s, stone milling was replaced by roller milling, which gave a quick separation of the bran and germ from the endosperm (the part of the grain that makes the white flour). By 1900, white bread had become the most commonly consumed bread in the world.

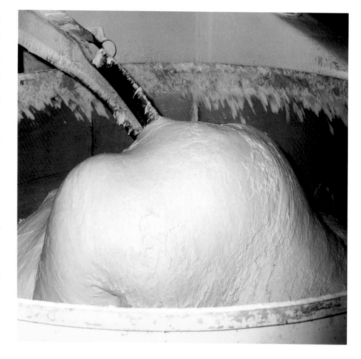

Major kinds of bread

People in North America and many European countries eat bread mainly baked as loaves or rolls made with wheat flour. In these countries, most of the bread is made by machines in large, commercial bakeries, although some bread making is still done in the home.

There are three main types of bread: yeast bread, quick bread, and flat bread. Yeast bread is raised by yeast. It is by far the most popular bread in North America and Europe. More than half of this type of bread consists of loaves of pan bread made with white flour. Pan bread is baked in a container and includes specialty breads such as raisin bread and whole wheat bread. Whole wheat bread is healthier than white bread, because the flour is made from the whole grain. It provides almost all of the natural vitamins and minerals of wheat and also contains fiber, which is an essential part of the human diet.

◀ **Bread comes in an endless variety of shapes and sizes—from small rolls and flat breads to large sandwich loaves and breadsticks. Bread can be made from different flours or mixes of flours. Many breads contain seeds or have seeds or nuts on top to add to their flavor.**

Quick bread is a type of bread often baked at home. The dough needs less time to prepare than yeast bread. Quick bread is raised by using baking powder or some other leaven (raising agent). Quick bread includes corn bread and muffins.

Flat bread is eaten in many parts of the world. It is usually thin and soft. It may be fried to make it crispy. Flat bread is made from grains such as barley, corn, oats, rice, rye, or wheat. In Central America, people eat cornmeal flat breads called tortillas. In China and other Asian countries, flat breads are made from rice flour. The Indian chapati flat bread is also made from corn flour. In the Middle East, pita is made from wheat.

Modern large-scale production

Many commercial bakeries make thousands of loaves at a time. The production begins when sifted flour enters the mixer from bags or storage machines. Water is then added, with carefully measured amounts of yeast, salt, and shortening (fat). All the ingredients are mixed to form a dough.

If the dough has to be fermented in bulk, it is left in a room kept at a constant temperature. After fermentation has taken place, the dough is cut into equal pieces by machine. If the dough has been fermented by machine or chemically, it is taken straight from the mixer and cut into pieces.

The dough pieces are taken on a conveyor belt to a machine that shapes them into balls. They are then dropped into pockets on a continuous belt situated in a warm, humid oven called a prover. Another conveyor takes the dough balls to a molding machine, which shapes them for the pans in which they are to be baked.

The filled pans are taken to a final prover, which is kept at a high temperature and humidity until the dough pieces are ready for baking. Baking takes place in a big tunnel-shaped oven. The dough passes slowly through the oven, and the bread is baked by the time it reaches the other end.

After cooling, the bread is conveyed to the slicing machine if it is to be sold sliced. The loaves are then picked up between metal plates to keep the slices together and are passed to a wrapping machine. The wrapped loaves of bread are then ready for delivery to shops and supermarkets.

See also: FOOD TECHNOLOGY • YEAST

Bridge

People built the first bridges more than two thousand years ago when they were needed to cross rivers and gorges. They learned how to build arch, beam, and suspension bridges. Now bridges have become part of our landscape, and people can cross them on foot, in cars, or in trains. There are even bridges for canal boats.

The simplest bridge is a log or slab of stone laid from bank to bank across a stream. This is called a beam bridge. If the stream is wide, a large stone in the middle may support the bridge. The support in the water is called the pier. The parts of the bridge stretching between the pier and the banks are called the spans.

Long ago, people also built suspension bridges. Vines or creepers sometimes grew across a valley from one tree to another. All people had to do was to wrap more vines around the existing vines to make a stronger cable. Another vine rope could be used to make a handrail. Today, the world's longest bridge spans are usually of the suspension kind.

The arch bridge
The finest early bridges were the Roman arch bridges. Some, such as the 98-foot- (30-meter-) long Alcantara Bridge over the Tagus River in Spain, have stood for nearly two thousand years.

Arch bridges are stronger than beam bridges. They work because each of the carefully shaped and angled stones is supported by the stones underneath, right down to the ground. The Romans built their bridges by starting at each side of the river and working toward the center. As each stone was placed on another, it jutted out slightly. The construction continued until the two halves met in the middle. Most Roman bridges were perfect semicircles.

Stones are heavy and difficult to work with. The first large arch bridge made of metal was built in 1779 at Coalbrookdale over the Severn River in Shropshire, Britain. Its span was 100 feet (30 meters). It was designed by English engineer Abraham Darby (1677–1717).

Since then, there have been many famous arch bridges. They are of two main types. In one type, the road or railroad runs over the top of the arch,

FORCES ACTING ON BRIDGES

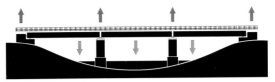

Beam bridge

Suspension bridge

Segmental arch bridge

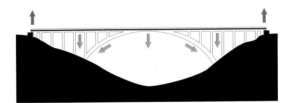

Semicircular arch bridge

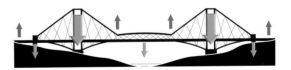

Cantilever bridge

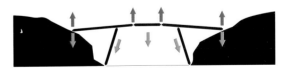

Modern cantilever bridge

▲ *Bridge design is based on the principle of balancing forces. The bridges with the greatest spans are all suspension bridges. Arch and cantilever bridge spans rarely exceed 1,700 feet (520 meters).*

◄ *The Pont de Gard in southern France is the finest surviving example of a Roman aqueduct. Aqueducts were bridges built to transport fresh water.*

231

such as in the bridge that spans Niagara Falls on the border between the United States and Canada. In the other type, the road runs below the arch, as in the Sydney Harbor Bridge in Australia. This bridge has a span of 1,650 feet (500 meters). The longest arch bridge in the world is the Lupu Bridge in Shanghai, China, which was completed in 2003. It is now the longest arch bridge in the world, with an arch spanning 1,815 feet (550 meters) and a total length of 12,870 feet (3,920 meters).

The suspension bridge

To build a suspension bridge, heavy cables are hung over concrete towers on each bank. The ends of the cables are securely fixed to the ground. Lighter cables hang from the main cables to support the roadway. The cables must be very strong. Each main cable of the Golden Gate Bridge in San Francisco is 36½ inches (1 meter) in diameter and contains 27,000 separate strands of wire.

The great weakness of suspension bridges is that they are liable to sway and vibrate in strong winds unless the bridge designers take careful precautions. In 1940, the Tacoma Narrows Bridge near Tacoma, Washington, swayed so much in

▲ *A photograph of the Tacoma Narrows Bridge taken after strong winds destroyed it on November 7, 1940.*

strong winds that it finally collapsed. Ten years later, a new, stronger bridge was built at the same spot at a cost of more than $18 million.

The world's largest spans are all made by suspension bridges. The Akashi Kaikyo Bridge in Japan has the longest span—one of 6,529 feet (1,990 meters). It is also the longest suspension bridge in the world, measuring 12,830 feet (3,911 meters) between anchorages. The Akashi Kaikyo Bridge joins Kobe to the offshore island Awaji.

Building bridges

Before a bridge is built, engineers have to decide on the best type of bridge for the site—suspension, beam, or arch. They must consider the materials to be used, the loads the bridge must carry, and the likelihood of high winds or earthquakes.

Most modern bridges are made from steel and reinforced concrete. Concrete is about four times heavier than steel for each unit of strength. To make the foundations for the bridge, caissons can be sunk into the river bed. Caissons are large, open-bottomed cylinders made of concrete or steel. When they have been sunk into the bed of the river, compressed air is pumped in, forcing water out of the caisson. Builders can then work in a dry atmosphere of compressed air to build the foundations for the bridge's supporting piers.

Nowadays, caissons are used less frequently in bridge building. Piers are now often supported on numbers of long piles, or thin-shelled cylinders. These piles may be 3 feet (1 meter) across and 165 feet (51 meters) long.

DID YOU KNOW?

The Tacoma Narrows Bridge disaster began when a support bracket on the central span slipped. This caused the vertical center cables to loosen, allowing the road bridge to twist in the wind. An amateur filmmaker caught the whole thing on camera. The disaster has been studied by engineers to ensure that nothing like it could happen again.

Erecting a bridge

A lot of thought goes into the construction of bridges. Can large pieces be brought into position from below? Or from above? Can the cranes be put in the right positions?

One of the simplest ways is to assemble a whole span in a workshop or on an area of level ground and then lift it into position in one piece. This can be done most easily, of course, for small bridges. However, some large structures have also been made in this way. The main span of the Ohnoura Bay Bridge in Japan is 640 feet (194 meters) long and weighs 1,000 tons (907 tonnes). It was put together in Tokyo, shipped in one piece for several hundred miles, and lowered gently onto its piers.

Bridges can also be built out from each end to meet in the middle. This is called cantilever construction. It is a very tricky method because the stresses are enormous as the bridge grows toward its center. During the construction of the Wye Bridge in Britain, the two halves of the main span—each measuring 770 feet (235 meters)—drooped by more than 10 feet (3 meters) as they met in the middle. Engineers had allowed for this so that the two halves could be joined smoothly.

Modern bridge building

The building of modern highways has caused the greatest bridge-building activity in the history of the world. In 1932, Sydney Harbor Bridge in Australia was opened. This was erected over deep water as two cantilevers until they met in the middle. Sydney Harbor Bridge is now the world's fourth widest long-span bridge.

The United States has some of the finest suspension bridges in the world. The Verrazano Narrows Bridge, built in 1964 at the entrance to New York Harbor, has steel towers 680 feet (207 meters) high and carries 12 lanes of traffic. Its span is 4,260 feet (1,298 meters). Due to the curvature of Earth's surface, the tops of the towers at each end of the bridge are 1.6 inches (4 centimeters) farther apart than their bases. The length of steel wire used to make the four main cables would stretch more than halfway to the Moon.

▲ *The Golden Gate Bridge is one of San Francisco's most famous landmarks.*

The Golden Gate Bridge in San Francisco was constructed between 1933 and 1937. It is still one of the world's most beautiful suspension bridges. The towers at either end support huge steel cables from which the bridge hangs. The center section between the towers is 4,200 feet (1,280 meters) long, and the bridge's six-lane highway is 220 feet (67 meters) above the water. The Golden Gate Bridge was the world's longest suspension bridge for nearly 30 years, until the construction of the Verrazano Narrows Bridge in New York.

See also: BUILDING TECHNIQUES

Broadcasting

Broadcasting is the transmission of signals over a broad area for people to pick up as sounds on their radios and images on their television sets. The first radio program was broadcast from Brant Rock, Massachusetts, on Christmas Eve, 1906. Television broadcasting started in 1928 with station WGY in New York.

When German scientist Heinrich Rudolph Hertz (1857–1894) discovered radio waves in 1887, people soon realized that messages could be transmitted without the need for a physical link, such as telegraph wires, between the sending and receiving equipment. In 1894, British scientist Oliver Lodge (1851–1940) demonstrated "wireless transmission" when he used radio waves to send a message over several hundred yards.

The first practical application of wireless transmission came in 1898, when Italian inventor Guglielmo Marconi (1874–1937) broadcast the results of a regatta from a tugboat in the Irish Sea. The message was sent as Morse code. Dots, dashes, and spaces, representing letters, numbers, and punctuation, were broadcast as electrical pulses to the offices of a newspaper in Dublin, Ireland.

Three years later, Marconi amazed the world when he sent wireless messages across the Atlantic Ocean between Britain and Canada. Soon it became possible to broadcast voice messages. At first, the new system was used to send private messages. However, the idea of using wireless for entertaining and informing the general public soon took hold, and radio broadcasting was born.

Radio broadcasting
The first radio program was broadcast from Brant Rock, Massachusetts, in 1906. It was Christmas Eve, and Canadian scientist Reginald Fessenden (1866–1932) transmitted music and Bible readings to wireless operators as far afield as Virginia. During World War I (1914–1918), experimental broadcasting stopped, and radio transmissions were reserved for vital wartime communications. The restriction was lifted after the war ended, and experimental broadcasting resumed.

Many people consider that the birth of modern radio broadcasting was on November 2, 1920. Station KDKA, Pittsburgh, went on the air to report the results of the presidential election, in which Warren Harding triumphed over James Cox. Just one year later, eight stations were broadcasting radio programs. By the end of 1922, 564 stations were competing for the public's attention.

▲ *Harry S. Truman, 33rd president of the United States, addresses the nation by radio on April 12, 1945, following the death of President Franklin D. Roosevelt.*

Meanwhile, in London Marconi started broadcasting using the call sign 2LO. This station inspired the British Post Office to have talks with radio equipment manufacturers to set up a broadcasting service to cover the whole country. This service was run by the British Broadcasting Company, which later became the British Broadcasting Corporation (BBC). Transmissions started in 1922, with three stations in London, Birmingham, and Manchester. The popularity of this new service meant that new stations soon opened in other regions.

Between 1925 and 1935, the number of broadcasting stations increased from about 600 to around 1,300 worldwide. The International Telecommunications Union was set up in 1932 to regulate this huge volume of radio traffic. This organization solved the problem of overcrowding and overlapping of radio wavelengths by allocating specific radio frequencies to different countries. By the early 1960s, there were at least 10,000 radio stations worldwide. Today, there are more than 13,300 stations in the United States alone.

Radio for the masses

In 1954, Texas Instruments and a company called IDEA designed and built the first portable transistor radio, the Regency TR-1. This invention, and the many different models that followed, made radio an accessible source of information for everyone—even poorer households. People could carry transistor radios in their pockets or listen to programs in their automobiles. At the end of World War II (1939–1945), there were 150 million radio sets worldwide. By the early 1970s, this figure had jumped to 820 million, most of which were cheap, portable transistor radios.

Television broadcasting

In 1926, British scientist and inventor John Logie Baird (1888–1946) transmitted a black-and-white image of a face onto a small screen. Baird's invention, originally called the "wireless vision" system, now entertains billions of people worldwide every day. Today, it is called the television.

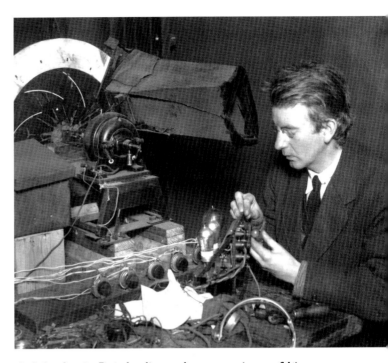

▲ *John Logie Baird adjusts the transmitter of his "wireless vision" system, now called the television.*

The images on a television screen consist of a series of lines. The definition (clarity) of the image depends on the number of lines used to make it. Baird's first images consisted of 30 lines. The definition was poor, and the lines themselves were very noticeable. In 1929, the definition improved by using 240 lines to make up the image. This was later increased to 405 for black-and-white images.

The first experimental television transmissions began in the United States in 1927. An audience in New York City watched an act performed by a comedian in Whippany, New Jersey. In the same year, John Logie Baird became the first person to broadcast television images across the Atlantic Ocean. He transmitted images of his own face using radio signals sent from London to New York. A year later, station WGY in New York started regular experimental transmissions to the general public.

In the United States, about 12 experimental television stations were set up in the 1930s. Drama, sports, and political programs were broadcast. The audience was small because there were no television sets on sale at the time. The only people with sets were those working for television companies, plus a few enthusiasts who built their own.

Television broadcasting expanded rapidly in the years following World War II (1939–1945). By 1948, 20 television stations were on the air in the United States, and hundreds more were applying for licenses to broadcast to the public.

Cable television

In the early days of television in the United States, most people relied on radio for entertainment. Television was a luxury for most households. During the late 1940s, however, the equipment became more affordable and more people tuned into television. People in big cities had no problem viewing programs on their television sets, but the reception for people in remote or hilly areas was poor. Television networks broadcast from antennas in the cities, and the signals could not reach remote places or pass through large hills. The development of Community Antenna Television (CATV), now called cable television, came from the need to provide clear signals to areas with poor reception.

▲ *A news reporter broadcasts a live transmission from the Iraqi Information Ministry roof during the 2003 Iraq War. Live broadcasts have been made possible by the development of satellite technology.*

The first cable systems were unreliable. Devices called amplifiers were needed at various points along the cable to boost the signal from the main antenna. If one of the amplifiers failed, the signals could not pass through the cable and the television picture would be lost.

Despite the initial problems, interest in cable television grew. In the 1950s, cable operators realized that they could use microwaves to transmit television signals instead of radio waves. Microwave signals could travel farther than radio signals. Viewers in New York could now watch programs broadcast from California. Since cable television started to offer viewers a wider range of programs, it became an attractive option for consumers in cities across the United States. Cable television soon became a national broadcasting phenomenon.

The popularity of cable television heralded a number of improvements to the system. Television manufacturers added a switch to new sets, so viewers could tune them either to conventional channels or the cable network. The problem of poor signal quality was solved when the old metal cables were replaced with fiber-optic cables. Fewer amplifiers are needed to boost signals carried on fiber-optic cables, so the reliability of the service improved. Fiber-optic cables can also carry more signals than metal cables, so the operators could serve more households at any one time. In addition, cable operators used fiber-optic cables to create local-area networks (LANs), providing a range of resources for individual neighborhoods, such as telephone services and Internet access.

Satellite television

In the 1960s, communications satellites provided a new and improved way of sending television signals. In 1962, the first television test transmissions by satellite were sent from the United States to Britain. From 1965, satellite links were used for broadcasting television programs.

Satellite communications have revolutionized television broadcasting. Networks in one country can now send signals from transmitters to satellites orbiting Earth. The satellites then beam the signals back to receivers worldwide. Some receivers are large dish-shaped antennas that serve entire television networks. The signals can then be distributed to individual viewers using radio waves, microwaves, or through a cable system. Many viewers now receive direct satellite transmissions through small dish antennas fixed to the exterior of their homes. In both cases, the signals pass to a set-top box connected to the television set. The set-top box decodes the signals and sends them to the correct channel on the television set.

▼ *Broadcasting from remote locations is now possible using videophones and satellite links.*

Digital television

A relatively new development in television broadcasting is digital television (DTV), or high-definition television (HDTV). DTV involves producing programs using digital cameras and equipment and transmitting the digital signals to viewers watching the programs using digital television sets. While the definition of an image on an older television, called an analog system, depends on the number of lines used to make it, DTV images consist of millions of tiny light squares called pixels. Each pixel controls the color and intensity of a tiny fraction of the image. Grouped together, the pixels produce crystal clear images on the screen. The sound quality of DTV is also much clearer than analog systems.

▼ *Newscasters Wendy Tokuda and Dave McElhatton prepare to go on the air on KPIX TV's* Eyewitness News *show in San Francisco.*

The governments of many countries have urged broadcasting companies to switch to DTV. In the United States, the Federal Communications Commission (FCC) asked every broadcasting company to change over to DTV by 2006. One of the main reasons for the switch is to improve the quality of television broadcasting, but there is also a financial incentive. Once broadcasters move over to DTV, the government plans to sell off the unused radio frequencies to cell-phone companies to bolster the federal budget.

Producing programs

In any live television studio, an array of cameras provides the primary source of visual material for the program being recorded. Sound comes from studio microphones hooked up to recording devices such as tape machines and turntables. In addition, there may be live broadcasting units, such

▲ *The London News Network control room prepares for a live broadcast. The control room is the heart of a television studio. The studio manager coordinates every part of the program, from camera angles to lighting effects, before it is transmitted to the public.*

as news reporters in the field, filming material and sending it back to the television studio using videophones and satellite links. Some parts of the program may be prerecorded on videotape using equipment called telecine machines. These recordings are then played at the appropriate part of the program.

Modern television studios have sophisticated editing facilities at their disposal to produce many different special effects. For example, chroma-key is a system that allows alternative backgrounds to be placed in the television image. Chroma-key is used during weather bulletins. It allows a series of computer-generated weather maps to be placed behind the forecaster during the broadcast.

During a live television broadcast, editors and production staff in the control room ensure that prerecorded material and live broadcasts are delivered on cue. The studio manager oversees the entire broadcast and controls effects such as camera directions, lighting, and recording levels.

Every program broadcast from a television network passes through a continuity suite. Here, a continuity announcer provides a continuous stream of broadcasting from a planned schedule and ensures that all programs run on time. Many networks insert advertisements in breaks between programs. From the continuity suite, the signals pass to regional transmitter stations and on to television sets in people's homes.

See also: ANTENNA • CABLE TELEVISION • COMMUNICATIONS SATELLITE • FIBER OPTICS • RADIO • TELEVISION • TRANSISTOR

Building techniques

People have always looked for places where they can sleep and take refuge from the elements. The first buildings were simple structures made from natural materials such as branches, mud, and straw. Today, towering skyscrapers dominate the skyline of cities throughout the world. These are possible because of the development of new materials and building techniques.

Early humans were hunter-gatherers. They led a nomadic existence, wandering in search of wild animals and collecting plants, fruits, and nuts they found on their way. These people did not need permanent shelters, so they took refuge in caves and under overhangs or built simple tents by stretching animal skins over strong branches sunk into the ground. Around 10,000 years ago, the world's first farmers started to grow crops and raise animals in regions including Mesopotamia (now modern-day Iraq), the Indus Valley, and Egypt. They built simple huts made from mud, straw, and turf piled up against branches. Around 6000 BCE, people around the Mediterranean Sea began to build permanent structures using mud bricks. The bricks were shaped in molds and left to dry in the Sun. The bricks were then stacked to make walls, using mud as a mortar to join them together.

Bronze Age builders

The next important development came around 3000 BCE with the discovery of an alloy called bronze. Bronze axes and saws could cut through hard materials such as wood and stone. Using these tools, the ancient Egyptians constructed the vast pyramids beside the Nile River as tombs for their pharaohs. Around the same time, some European civilizations began to build wooden houses. At the same time, the wheel came into use, and potters realized that their kilns could produce hard-baked and durable clay bricks.

Classical designs

Building techniques had come a long way by the time of the ancient Greeks and Romans. Greek engineers developed pulleys to lift heavy weights. Greek architects used geometry and trigonometry to design beautiful marble structures.

The Romans first began to use arches in many of their buildings. Triumphal arches, bridges, and aqueducts still stand as a reminder of the skill of these early Roman builders. As their buildings became larger, and the span between arches wider, Roman engineers developed the semicircular arch. This could support a greater load than the flat stone lintel common in Greek buildings.

◀ *The pyramids of Giza, Egypt, were begun around 2560 BCE. Pharaoh Khufu's Great Pyramid (center) is believed to have taken 20 years to build, employing as many as 30,000 workers in its construction.*

DID YOU KNOW?

Experts think that the Great Pyramid of Khufu has more than two million limestone blocks in its structure. Each block weighs an average of 2½ tons (2.2 tonnes), with the maximum being 15 tons (13.6 tonnes). Before each block was placed, it was worked to a 52-degree angle to make the sloping sides of the pyramid even. The capstone at the very top was a tiny version of the pyramid itself. The capstone was made of granite and was often covered in gold.

▲ *Designed in 1850 in the Gothic tradition of European churches of the twelfth to fifteenth centuries, St. Patrick's Cathedral in New York City stands out among the city's other, modern architecture. Gothic buildings are characterized by pointed arches, rib vaulting, and an emphasis on height.*

The Romans also developed concrete as a basic building material. Bricks were used as a backing for decorative mosaic tiles.

Gothic buildings

The fall of the Roman Empire prompted a major setback to the progress of building technology. Few of the Roman techniques survived, and buildings lacked the strength provided by concrete. In the Middle Ages, European architects wanted to build impressive stone structures as tall as possible, but they faced many problems. Stone is a heavy material. The architects found it difficult to design buildings with tall walls and vast roofs that could support their own weight.

The construction of Durham Cathedral in England, which started in 1093, solved the problem. It was built using tall, pointed arches, called vaults, in the roof. Massive supports called flying buttresses were used to prop up the walls from the outside and give the building extra strength. This style of architecture, known as Gothic, became popular throughout Europe between the twelfth and fifteenth centuries.

Buildings from the East

Some of the first builders were farmers in Mesopotamia and the Indus Valley. Around 10,000 years ago, these farmers built simple homes to shelter their families while they tended to crops and livestock. By 2000 BCE, these small agricultural settlements had turned into large cities, with buildings laid out in a grid pattern and constructed from brick. From 1000 BCE, simpler buildings were constructed. They consisted of timber posts and beams enclosed with wattle (intertwined branches) and plaster or bricks. Temples were made from beautifully carved stone and built up into pyramid-like structures.

In China, very little exists that was built earlier than the twelfth century. Hard-packed earth, sometimes faced with brick, formed the base of

◀ The five-story pagoda at the Buddhist Daigoji Temple complex in Kyoto, Japan. Built in 951 CE, it is one of the oldest pagodas in Japan. Pagodas are built as shrines and contain very little usable interior space.

clay, woven and felted fibers, and metal. The designs allowed for disasters such as earthquakes and storms, which frequently affected the country.

BUILDING MATERIALS

Over the years, many different materials have been used for building construction. Modern construction still relies on traditional materials such as timber and brick. But many new materials, such as metals, glass, plastics, and carbon fiber are now also common.

Timber building techniques

Wood is one of the oldest building materials. Up to the fifteenth century, most domestic structures were built around a timber frame. Roman country villas were constructed on a squared timber framework. Cruck frames came into use during the eighth and ninth centuries. They were curved and formed the main support of the roof, but they limited the design of the building. Balloon frames solved this problem. They were made up of lighter timbers nailed together. Balloon frames are still in use today.

▼ This traditional log cabin is being constructed in Norway. The availability of raw materials, labor, and building equipment has ensured that different building techniques have developed around the world.

early Chinese buildings. Wooden columns were set above the base and joined with beams. To support the roof, beams of decreasing size were placed one above the other, unlike the rigid triangular framework developed in Europe. Bamboo brackets were used to extend the rafters beyond the columns. The roofs came in one of three basic designs. They were decorated with glazed tiles in striking blues, yellows, and greens.

The pagoda and other typical Japanese designs were copied from Chinese architecture. Japanese builders drew on natural materials, such as timber,

Wood is still a very useful material in modern construction. New adhesives stand up to heat and moisture, so thin sheets of wood can be glued together to form plywood. Arranging the grain in the various layers so that it runs in different directions gives plywood greater strength. It also means that wood can be formed into beamlike sections, or trusses, to span much larger spaces than was possible before.

▼ *The most basic bricklaying arrangement of all, called the stretcher bond, has been modified to produce stronger, more attractive brick walls. The English bond incorporates alternate courses of stretcher (long face visible) and header (short face visible) bricks. The Flemish bond has alternating stretchers and headers in every course.*

Brickmaking

The first bricks were lumps of mud shaped by hand and dried in the Sun until they became hard. Later, brickmakers shaped bricks by ramming wet mud into a wooden rectangular frame. Then they lifted the frame off, which left a rectangular brick on the ground, ready for drying. This process seems to have spread quickly throughout the Middle East. By about 4,500 years ago, the Mesopotamians had started to fire (bake) bricks to make them harder. Fuel for firing was very scarce, so fired bricks were usually saved for use on arches, cornerstones, window and door frames, and facades (fronts).

The Romans were master brickmakers. They also developed a strong cement mixture (mortar) to join their bricks together. Most Roman bricks were fired in furnaces called kilns. But bricks in Roman times did not look like those of today. They were more like tiles—around 18 inches (46 centimeters) long, 12 inches (30 centimeters) wide, and 1 inch (2.5 centimeters) thick. In the United States, the standard brick size is now 8 inches (20 centimeters) long, 3¾ inches (9 centimeters) wide and 2¼ inches (6 centimeters) thick.

Building with bricks

Bricks are laid so that each brick overlaps the one below it. This means that the vertical joints are staggered, making a stronger structure. Bricks used for building are held together with mortar. Today,

BRICKLAYING TECHNIQUES

Stretcher bond

English bond

Flemish bond

MANUFACTURING PORTLAND CEMENT

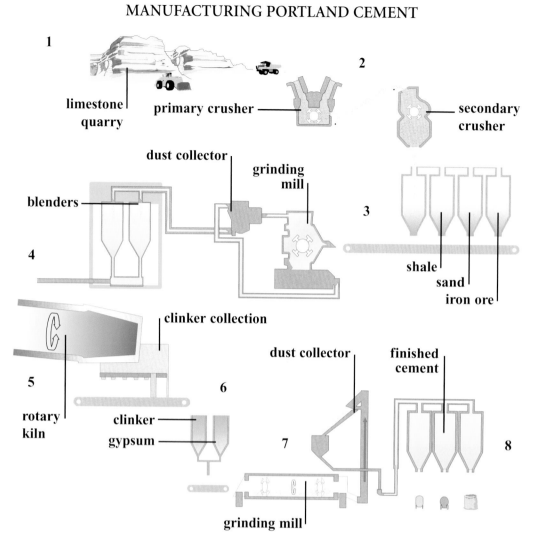

1 limestone quarry
primary crusher
2 secondary crusher
dust collector
grinding mill
blenders
4
3 shale
sand
iron ore
clinker collection
5 rotary kiln
6 clinker
gypsum
dust collector
finished cement
7 grinding mill
8

◀ *1. One of the primary components of cement is limestone.*
2. The quarried rocks are crushed in two stages.
3. The limestone is mixed with shale (a sedimentary rock), sand, and iron ore in controlled proportions. The mixture is ground to form a fine powder.
4. The powder is then blended. In the wet process, it is blended in water; in the dry process, it is mechanically blended and may be preheated.
5. The mixture is loaded into a rotary kiln and undergoes different chemical reactions in different temperature zones. It partially melts to form a dense clinker.
6. The clinker is collected, then mixed with gypsum.
7. The clinker and gypsum mixture is finely ground to form cement.
8. The cement may be transported by truck or rail or bagged on site.

mortar is usually made of sand, Portland cement, and lime (calcium oxide; CaO). The cement holds the other parts of the mortar together.

Early forms of cement

The ancient Egyptians were the first builders to use mortar. They developed a mixture containing gypsum, which is commonly known as plaster of Paris. Like most other forms of cement, it hardens when water is added to it.

The Greeks and Romans used slaked lime (calcium hydroxide; $Ca(OH)_2$) as mortar in many of their buildings, but it tended to crack and crumble when exposed to extremes of weather. Then they discovered how to make a much more durable mortar from lime, sand, and a material from volcanoes called pozzolana. (Pozzolana is

named after the Italian town of Pozzuoli, where much of it was found.) When water was added to this mortar, the pozzolana and lime bound the sand grains together. This hard mortar was used to build both the Pantheon and the Colosseum in Rome. It remained in use until the late eighteenth century.

In 1824, Joseph Aspdin took out a patent in England on a process for making Portland cement, so named for its resemblance to the limestone quarried on the Isle of Portland in Britain. Portland cement is widely used today. It produces a very strong mortar when mixed with sand and water.

Cement chemistry

The main ingredients of Portland cement are four anhydrous calcium compounds. (The term *anhydrous* means that the compounds contain no water.) When water is added to the cement, chemical reactions take place. Long, needlelike crystals form and lock together, binding the cement into a hard, strong mass. A small amount of gypsum in the cement prevents it from setting too quickly when the water is added. This makes the cement much easier to use.

Making cement

Cement is usually made near the quarries that supply the raw materials. Chalk or limestone is used as a source of calcium compounds. Clay or shale provides aluminum silicates. Cement can be made by either a wet or a dry process. The wet process is used where the raw materials are chalk and clay. Water is added and they are blended to form a muddy mixture called a slurry. In the dry process, harder raw materials, such as limestone and shale, are crushed and blended. In both cases, the ingredients are then fed into a kiln. The kiln operates at a temperature of 2700°F (1500°C). The kiln turns slowly, and a stream of air passes over the cement mixture. The heat partly melts the materials, and they emerge as lumps of what is called cement clinker. To prepare powdered cement, about 2 percent of gypsum is first added to the clinker. The mixture is then ground into a very fine powder called Portland cement.

Concrete constituents

Concrete is a mixture of aggregate, cement, and water. Aggregate consists of coarse material, such as stones or gravel, mixed with fine material, such as sand. When water is added to this mixture, it can be molded into almost any shape before the concrete sets hard. Concrete does not always contain the same amount of aggregate, cement, and water. Generally, the more cement in the mixture, the stronger the concrete. The more water in the mixture, the more pliable the concrete.

Mixing, pouring, and curing

Most concrete is now mixed by a machine. When the concrete is ready, it is often poured into place using a pipe and pump. This ensures that the concrete has the right texture and removes excess air bubbles, which would weaken the structure.

The next stage is curing. This ensures that the concrete sets in the right way. Concrete does not harden by drying out; it hardens by a chemical process. During that time, the concrete must be sprinkled with water or covered with polyethylene sheets to keep it moist.

Concrete construction

Concrete's importance as a building material comes from its ability to withstand enormous pressures. Originally, concrete was best suited to bearing great weights because it did not disintegrate under pressure—it was ideal for building foundations. However, it was not able to withstand sideways or bending pressures until the introduction of reinforced and prestressed concrete, which have greater tensile strength. Reinforced and prestressed concrete can be used for most construction work, because they keep their shape and strength under different sorts of pressure.

Reinforced or prestressed?

Reinforced concrete has steel wires and rods embedded in it. It can be cast in any shape, as long as the steel is bent to the correct shape before the concrete sets around it. Almost all concrete used today is reinforced.

Prestressed concrete is even more flexible than reinforced concrete. The steel it contains is stretched to such a degree that the concrete will be out of shape until the required load is in place. This tension can be put into the steel before the concrete is cast or afterward (post-tensioning).

Iron and steel

Modern building techniques developed from the birth of the Industrial Revolution, which began toward the end of the eighteenth century. The completion of the Iron Bridge over the Severn River at Coalbrookdale, Britain, in 1779 led to the use of iron and steel as a basic framework for most structures. By the end of the nineteenth century, rolled steel beams were readily available. Rivets and bolts provided easy methods of assembling them. A later development used arc welding, in which an electric current melts the edges of the steel together to form a strong bond.

MODERN CONSTRUCTION

Technological developments in the twentieth century have seen many buildings designed with new materials such as aluminum, fiberglass, and plastics. Concrete and steel are the most important modern building materials. Traditional materials, such as brick and wood, are still very popular.

The first stages

A major building project will start with the design, which is carried out by architects and engineers. These people make sure that the structure will stand up to the tasks required. Construction itself requires many different machines, as well as the workers who operate them. The workers also provide the skills and labor to carry out the jobs that the machines cannot do.

First to arrive on the site are the earthmoving machines—bulldozers, excavators, and scrapers. Their job is to clear the site and then move the earth into the proper shape with holes and flat areas made where they are needed.

Laying the foundations

A building must have a firm base or it will sink into the ground under its own weight. So the next step is establishing firm foundations for the structure. Builders often have to construct foundations. In one type, holes are dug or drilled into the ground and filled with concrete, which is sometimes poured into long metal cylinders. These columns are called piles and provide a steady base in the same way that a stick thrust deep into a pile of loose sand will stand upright. In another kind of foundation, walls of concrete are driven into the ground and a concrete floor laid between them so that the building rises from this ground-supported box. In some cases, a solid concrete slab is built over a wide area of soil, spreading the load, with the building itself rising up from just one part.

▲ *This ultramodern building is the Guggenheim Museum in Bilbao, Spain. Built on a steel frame, it is covered with titanium cladding.*

Frame construction

The builders then construct a frame for the building. In some designs, the load-bearing frame stands around the outside edges of the building. In others, a central core takes the structure's weight.

Timber frames are still very often used for houses and other small buildings. The frames are usually made of rectangular wooden slats connected by nails or bolts. Large structures became possible when steel began to be used for frames. Sections of metal and concrete frames are bolted, riveted, or welded together on site. As the structure grows, cranes are built up to lift and position materials. The floors are put in, together with pipes, ducts, and wiring to provide drains, water, and electricity.

When all the floors have been built, the whole frame is covered on the outside. Most commercial buildings, such as offices and hotels, use glass, stone, or metal of some kind. Private homes are more often covered with brick, glass, or wood.

High-rise buildings

High-rise buildings, or skyscrapers, have grown up to house as many people as possible where there is limited ground space. Manhattan in New York City is one example, as are the thriving cities of Hong Kong and Singapore in Southeast Asia.

Very tall buildings present many technical design problems. Sweeping winds create unusual and disturbing conditions near tall buildings. Some high-rise buildings are so high that the temperature and weather at the top can be very different from those at the bottom, adding to the stresses.

In certain parts of the world, earthquakes are another natural hazard. Modern earthquake-resistant building designs are based on the findings of architects and engineers after years of studying violent ground motion and its effect on tall buildings. Reinforced concrete or steel frames are required, and there can be no stone trimmings, as they can be shaken off by heavy tremors.

Fire is a constant worry. Lightning conductors protect against lightning's electrical discharges. Strict regulations about building materials, placement of ducts, and water supplies, also provide a high level of protection.

Tensile structures

Some of the largest modern buildings in the world are being constructed like huge tents. Tensile structures are made of flexible materials stretched over frames or hung from poles. The stretched, curving roofs keep the weather out and give light and warmth to the people underneath. This modern form of tent provides excellent space, light, and ease of construction compared to traditional buildings. A tensile structure can be either permanent or temporary. It can be taken down as easily as it was put up, and it can be moved to a new place if needed.

Computer programs help to find the best shapes for tensile structures. The designer supplies information about the strength of the fabric to be used and the spacing of the supports. The computer then draws on the screen and shows the ideal shape for the building. This shape can be tested and changed by typing in new figures.

▶ *Skyscrapers are found in cities, where space to build is limited. They can hold many people on a relatively small area of land. The Taipei 101 building in Taipei, Taiwan, is the tallest in the world. It stands 1,676 feet (508 meters) tall.*

Permanent tensile structures

The most common fabric used for permanent tensile structures is woven fiberglass with a Teflon nonstick coating. The strength of the fabric comes from the thin, woven glass fibers. Dust and dirt cannot pass into the weave of Teflon-coated fiberglass, so they are either blown away by the wind or washed away by rain. This makes the fabric virtually self-cleaning. The Teflon-coated fiberglass does not burn and has good resistance to heat, water, and chemicals.

Temporary tensile structures

Polyester coated with polyvinyl chloride (PVC) is the most common material used for the roof of temporary structures. This fabric is light, flexible,

and stretches enough to absorb small inaccuracies without showing wrinkles. Polyester is easily taken down, folded, stored and reused. But there are disadvantages to vinyl-coated polyester. In a fire, for instance, PVC fabric gives off thick black smoke that makes it unsuitable for permanent structures. Also, polyester fabrics continue to stretch while they are under tension and will lose their tensile properties over time.

"GREEN" ARCHITECTURE

People now realize that poorly designed buildings waste energy and can even make their occupants ill. "Green" architecture means designing buildings that use as little fuel as possible and do not harm the environment.

Intelligent buildings

If a building is designed carefully, it does not need much heating, even in cooler climates. This approach relies on the Sun and wind to heat or cool spaces directly. Buildings may have unusual shapes to make the best use of the natural surroundings. Massive walls and floors can store heat in winter and keep the building cool in summer. The windows and openings are placed to let in the most sunshine or breeze.

Computers now link up to virtually every aspect of a modern building's operation. By switching equipment on before people enter the building, energy may actually be saved. On the other hand, a computer may be able to turn off the lights and heating in rooms that are used only at certain times of the day. This way, buildings use less energy to produce the same results.

Noisy buildings

One way to stop sound from passing between rooms is to use thick, heavy walls and floors. Concrete and brick are heavy and so block out sounds very well. When lighter materials are used for walls, they should be as stiff as possible.

A layer of air between two panels can help keep out noise. Double-glazed windows, for example, have two layers of glass separated by air. It is important that such windows be kept tightly shut, as soundproofing will not work if there are any gaps. Good soundproofing needs special air vents to let in fresh air without letting in noise.

Soft, absorbent materials such as foam rubber help to deaden noise. Classrooms and offices can be made quieter by covering hard smooth surfaces. Carpets can be used on floors, for example.

"Sick" buildings

Many modern buildings pose a significant health risk. People in them may complain of minor diseases and ailments. This problem is known as "sick building syndrome." It may be caused by poor ventilation, lack of outside views, or overheating. Gases given off by building materials can also be to blame. Pollution can build up unnoticed, coming either from building materials or even from the ground itself. Radon is a dangerous gas emitted by the rocks in some areas. If the building is badly ventilated, maybe in an attempt to insulate it, the radon may not be able to escape. The answer is to build a well-ventilated gap below the ground floor.

DEMOLITION

Knocking down buildings (demolition) has been going on for as long as buildings have been put up. Many buildings are demolished in crowded towns and cities, and today safe demolition often requires specialized skills and techniques to avoid damaging nearby structures or endangering their residents.

The chief ways of demolishing a structure are usually by dismantling it piece by piece, pulling it down or pushing it over, making it collapse under its own weight (often helped by explosives), knocking it down with sledgehammers or a heavy demolition ball, or by using various combinations of these methods.

Hand demolition

Demolition of buildings by the use of hand tools such as sledgehammers and pneumatic drills is usually carried out in the reverse order of the way in which the building was built. Small structures may be taken down entirely by hand. Taller

structures, such as cooling towers and smokestacks, may have only their upper sections demolished by hand. When the height of the structure has been sufficiently reduced, it can be safely brought down by demolition balls or pushers.

Mechanical demolition

The demolition ball is a widely used means of knocking down buildings. It is a heavy, pear-shaped, cast-steel weight suspended from a crane or dragline excavator. The ball is swung against or dropped onto the structure being demolished. However, demolition balls cannot usually be safely used on structures much over 100 feet (30 meters) in height, as debris could be thrown over a large area.

A pusher arm can be used to knock over brick or masonry structures. Pusher arms are fitted to large hydraulic excavators in place of their buckets and are usually about 15 feet (5 meters) long. Some pushers have a reach of about 45 feet (14 meters).

Structures can also be brought down by pulling them in key areas with a wire rope or ropes attached to a tracked vehicle or a fixed winch.

▲ **Old apartments are demolished with explosives to make way for a new development. Such buildings are often built cheaply and can have a limited lifespan.**

Collapsing buildings

Sometimes, when the site is well away from other buildings, demolition can be carried out by removing key parts at the bottom of the building, causing it to collapse under its own weight. This can be dangerous and needs expert supervision.

One of the best ways of making a building collapse is by the use of explosives. Charges are placed at the base of the building's supporting walls. When they explode the structure collapses inward.

When large blocks of concrete have to be broken up, but it is not possible to use explosives, bursters can be used. These are charges in steel tubes that do not explode when they are detonated, but expand outward with great force, breaking up the concrete.

See *also*: ARCHITECTURE • BRIDGE • ENGINEERING • SKYSCRAPER

Cable television

Cable television started life in the 1950s. It provided clear television signals to remote areas with poor reception by means of a cable instead of an antenna. Today, cable networks deliver hundreds of channels to more than 90 million homes in the United States. Many networks offer people high-speed access to the Internet, and some let people make telephone calls.

In the early days of television, around the late 1940s, people watched programs on three main networks broadcast from transmitting antennas in large cities. People who lived in remote or hilly regions could not watch television programs. The signals could not pass through objects such as big hills, and the reception in these areas was very poor.

In June 1948, a television salesman named John Walson solved the problem by installing an antenna on top of a hill near his store in Mahanoy City, Pennsylvania. The antenna received the signals transmitted from the main television antennas in Philadelphia. Walson then routed the signals along a cable running from the antenna on the hill down to the televisions in his store. People saw the improvement in picture quality, and the sale of televisions in Walson's store soared.

Developing technology

When televisions first went on sale, every set needed a separate antenna to receive signals from the main television transmitters. The roofs of department stores selling television sets were covered with antennas. To reduce the number of antennas on the roofs, U.S. electronics engineer Milton Jerrold Shapp developed a master antenna television (MATV) system in the early 1950s. His system used a coaxial cable and signal boosters, called amplifiers, to carry multiple signals along the same cable at the same time. Shapp realized that his MATV system could be used to distribute signals to more than one television set in a town as well as a department store. Shapp developed a MATV

◄ Fans on the set of the MTV show **Total Request Live** at the studios in Times Square, New York. MTV broadcasts many different programs dedicated to particular types of music and entertainment, from **Hip-Hop Countdown** to **The Osbournes**. Other cable channels cover topics ranging from world news and weather to sports, education, and public affairs.

distribution system and sold his new technology to towns and cities across the United States. Community Antenna Television (CATV), or cable television as it is now called, was born.

Sending the signals

A multipair cable contains several pairs of wires. Each pair is used to carry one television program. To view the programs, a special set must be used. Unlike an ordinary television set, it has no tuning unit to select the programs. Instead, it has a selector switch. This connects the set to any pair of wires in the cable and thus selects the program.

A typical cable carries six programs. So, where a large number of programs are required, several cables must be used. The cable costs are, therefore, fairly high. On the other hand, the simple receivers used with this system are relatively cheap.

An ordinary television set uses an antenna to pick up several programs. A tuning unit in the set selects the required program. A cable system can be made to work in a similar way but, instead of transmitting the programs from an antenna, they are all sent along a single cable called a coaxial cable. It has a center wire with a surrounding metal braid. It can carry many television signals transmitted over a wide range of frequencies.

With this system, the television set must have a tuning unit to select the programs. This makes it more expensive than the type used with the multipair system. However, the cable costs are much lower because all the programs are sent along the same wire.

In other systems, the viewer turns a dial connected to one cable. The required program is then automatically sent to the home via another cable. Bidirectional systems allow the viewer to respond to questions put on the screen. You may be asked to vote in a debate or to choose a happy or sad ending for the movie you are watching.

Broadening horizons

Cable television was originally designed to improve reception in remote areas, so people could watch clear programs broadcast from the local television

▲ *A cross section through a bundle of coaxial cables contained within one sheath. Each cable consists of a solid central conductor surrounded by an insulator and covered by a cylindrical shield woven from fine wires.*

networks. The pioneers of cable television soon realized that microwaves could be used to transmit signals from distant cities. They built huge towers to transmit and receive the microwave signals. Now a viewer in Pennsylvania could watch programs broadcast in New York or California.

Although most big cities had a good television service, cable networks became more attractive to the consumer. They offered clearer reception and a wider range of programs made for a particular interest, such as sports or rock music. Viewers could watch the programs at any time, because the cable operators could send dozens of television signals along the same cable. Consequently, cable television moved into the cities and opened up viewing choices for most Americans.

However, microwave links were expensive, and a large number of transmitters were needed to cover the country. So, toward the end of the 1960s, it seemed that the cable television would not be able to expand further. Then, in 1972, the Federal Communications Commission (FCC) found a solution to the problem. They granted permission for private companies to own and operate communications satellites.

Satellite links

Communications satellites move around Earth 22,300 miles (36,000 kilometers) above the equator. These satellites keep up with Earth as it spins, so they appear to hover motionless above some point on the equator. These satellites are said to be in geosynchronous orbit. The television signals are sent from transmitters on Earth to the satellite, which then beams the signals back to receivers on Earth. The signals sent back to Earth can cover an area of millions of square miles.

Distribution through satellites revolutionized cable television. In 1972, John Walson's company, Service Electric, launched Home Box Office (HBO) over its cable network. HBO—the first in a long line of "pay TV" stations—was originally distributed by a terrestrial microwave system. It later became the first service to distribute programs

using communications satellites. Following in the footsteps of HBO, Ted Turner created the WTBS station broadcasting from Atlanta—the first "superstation"—and followed it with the launch of Central News Network (CNN). Now there are around 200 networks distributed by satellite, and the number is increasing. The networks cover everything from education, health, and public affairs to music, shopping, and sports.

An increasing number of homes are now equipped with dish antennas to receive direct satellite-to-home television transmissions. This change could affect technology so greatly that all other systems, such as broadcasting stations and cable systems, may not be needed any more.

Fiber optics

In 1976, engineers developed fiber-optic cables to carry signals from the CATV distribution stations to neighborhoods. One of the main advantages of fiber-optic cabling is that it does not suffer the same signal losses as coaxial cables. Signals become weaker as they pass along coaxial cables, so amplifiers need to be placed at various points along the cable to boost the signals. If one of the amplifiers breaks down, the picture is lost.

With fiber-optic cabling, fewer amplifiers are needed to boost the signals. As a result, signal quality and the reliability of cable services improved. Another advantage of fiber-optic cabling is that one cable can serve many more households than conventional coaxial cabling. Cable providers can therefore target individual neighborhoods with specific messages and services.

Cable providers soon realized that the cable network was an ideal medium for creating local-area networks (LANs) to provide a range of different services. These include telephone services, video communication and conferencing, high-speed Internet access, home shopping and banking, and many other resources.

▲ *Most cable networks use satellites to send programs to all parts of a country. Each community served by the system has a dish-shaped antenna to pick up the signals. A receiver connected to the antenna separates the television signals. These are distributed locally by cable.*

◀ *A lineman installs a new overhead cable. As well as being carried by overhead poles, cables can be run through underground trunking.*

See also: ANTENNA • BROADCASTING • COMMUNICATIONS SATELLITE • RADIO • TELEVISION

253

Glossary

Biodegradable Capable of being decomposed by biological agents, especially bacteria.

Carburetor A device used in older internal combustion engines to produce an explosive mixture of fuel vapor (mist) and air.

Cell membrane A thin, flexible layer of tissue covering the surface of a cell.

Corrosion The breakdown in metals caused by oxidation (oxygen reaction) or chemical action.

Digital In communication, the representation of information as numbers. In computer technology, the representation of numbers as discrete units.

Ecosystem An interdependent community of living organisms functioning together within its nonliving environment as a unit.

Fiber optics The transmission of light signals through glass fibers.

Friction The resistance encountered when one body is moved in contact with another.

Gasoline A volatile, flammable mixture derived from petroleum. Used mainly as a fuel.

Gene A hereditary unit consisting of a segment of DNA (deoxyribonucleic acid). Each gene occupies a specific location on a chromosome (a threadlike body made of DNA in the cell nucleus) and determines a particular characteristic in an organism.

Genetic engineering The joining together of genetic material, especially DNA, from one or more species of organism, and the introduction of the result into an organism to change one or more of its characteristics.

Geometry The mathematics of the properties, measurement, and relationships of angles, lines, points, solids, and surfaces.

Gravity The natural force of attraction exerted by a massive body, such as Earth, upon objects at or near its surface, tending to draw the objects toward the center of the body.

Horsepower A unit of power equal to 745.7 watts or 33,000 foot-pounds per minute. Used, in particular, to rate the power of engines.

Hydraulics The science and technology of the static and dynamic behavior of fluids, especially in relation to the control and management of water and the use of fluids to operate machines.

Hydrodynamics The branch of physics that deals with the motion of fluids and the forces acting on solid bodies immersed in fluids.

Hydrostatics The branch of physics that deals with fluids at rest and the pressures they exert or transmit under pressure.

Internal combustion engine A heat engine in which the combustion that generates the heat takes place inside the engine itself.

Ion An atom or a group of atoms that has acquired an overall electric charge by gaining or losing one or more electrons.

Isotope Any of two or more forms of a chemical element with the same atomic number but different nuclear masses.

Light-year The distance that light travels in a vacuum in one year—approximately 5.88 trillion miles or 9.46 trillion kilometers.

Microorganism An organism, such as a bacterium, that is too small to be seen with the naked eye.

Pneumatic Run by or using compressed air, or filled with air (especially compressed air).

Protists Any of the unicellular (single-celled) plant- and animal-like organisms and their descendant multicellular (many-celled) organisms.

Radiation Energy radiated or transmitted as rays, waves, or in the form of particles. Visible light is an example of radiation.

Trigonometry The branch of mathematics that deals with the relationships between the sides and the angles of triangles.

Vacuum A space entirely devoid of matter, or more generally, a space that has been exhausted to a high degree by an air pump or other artificial means.

X-ray Short-wave electromagnetic radiation produced when speeding electrons hit a solid target.

Index

Page numbers in **bold** refer to main articles; those in *italics* refer to illustrations.

Index

Page numbers in **bold** refer to main articles; those in *italics* refer to illustrations.